KEEPING THE PROMISE

A Pictorial History Of
The Miami Conservancy District

By Carl M. Becker and Patrick B. Nolan

Landfall Press
Dayton, Ohio
1988

KEEPING THE PROMISE

A Pictorial History of the Miami Conservancy District
by Carl M. Becker and Patrick B. Nolan

Copyright © 1988 by the Miami Conservancy District

Published by Landfall Press, Inc., 5171 Chapin St., Dayton,
Ohio 45429

ISBN 0-913428-65-5 clothbound; 0-913428-66-3 paperback
Library of Congress Catalog Card No. 87-081625

DEDICATED
To the People of the Miami Valley,
Who Endured and Who Built

At the first meeting of the Miami Conservancy District's Board of Directors, July 7, 1915, Edward A. Deeds announced he would build and donate to the District a headquarters building. Contracts were let on August 7 and by the following January 8 the building (above) was occupied as the Conservancy's permanent home. On April 28, 1918, Col. and Mrs. Deeds formally conveyed the building to the District as a gift. Standing at the corner of Jefferson Street and Monument Avenue in downtown Dayton, where it overlooks the Great Miami River, the building has been in use ever since.

Table of Contents

The Lay of the Land and Its History 15

And the Waters Prevailed 23

Balm in Gilead: Rescue, Relief and Recovery 41

Make Miami Valley Mighty 105

Building for the Ages 115

Sustaining the System 185

Figures

Figure 1. The Great Miami River Basin 16

Figure 2. The Wisconsin Glacier 18

Figure 3. The 1913 Flood in Dayton 24

Figure 4. The Rivers, Counties and Principal Cities of the
           Miami Conservancy District 111

Figure 5. The Dams of the Miami Conservancy District 112

Appendices

Appendix A. Explanation of Assessment Methods of
             Miami Conservancy District 194

Appendix B. Conservancy Court Judges,
             Miami Conservancy District 200

Appendix C. Board of Directors, Miami Conservancy District 201

Appendix D. Chief Engineers and General Managers,
             Miami Conservancy District 202

Appendix E. Boards of Consultants, Miami Conservancy District 203

Appendix F. 1913 Flood gradients in Dayton 204

Appendix G. 1913 Flood gradients in Hamilton 205

Appendix H. Ten highest floods, 1893-1913 206

Appendix I. Projected 1959 Highwater, Hamilton-Dayton 207

Additional Reading

Readers interested in learning more about the great flood of 1913, the consequent creation of the Miami Conservancy District and its construction of the conservancy system, will not find an abundance of published sources.

For the coming of the flood and its devastating effects in Dayton, Allan W. Eckert has painted a vivid, though sometime quasi-fictional, portrait in his book, *A Time of Terror* (Landfall Press, Inc., Dayton, 1973).

In John C. Hover, ed., *Memoirs of the Miami Valley* (Robert O. Law Company, Chicago, 1919), one may find detailed and dramatic accounts of the flood as it struck communities throughout the Miami Valley.

Depending on the community one is interested in, the reader may find ephemera of various kinds in local libraries: oral histories, newspaper clippings, booklets, etc. Among these publications one could cite, for example, Nellis R. Funk, *A Pictorial History of the Great Dayton Flood* (The Otterbein Press, Dayton, 1913).

On the creation of the Miami Conservancy District and the subsequent construction of dams and levees, a subject that cries for a comprehensive history, one can discover little in published works. Fortunately, near the end of his career, Arthur Morgan wrote a kind of memoir-history, *The Miami Conservancy District* (McGraw-Hill Book Company, Inc., New York, 1951). It is quite useful and interesting at points. But it does not preempt the subject, lacking as it does at points coherency and comprehensiveness.

L. Bennett Coy, former General Manager of the District, has written a very brief but useful article on the origins and operations of the District in "History and Operations of Miami Conservancy District," (*Journal of American Water Works Association*, 58, April 1966, 403-407). Among ephemera worthwhile consulting is a booklet published in 1947, *Lest We Forget*, by the Dayton Chamber of Commerce.

Students interested in the activities of the District during a particular year, in the progress of special projects over several years, or in financial data, should consult the annual reports of the District and of the Chief Engineer. These reports, various special reports, and other records bearing on the history of the District, are available at the District headquarters and at the Archives and Special Collections at Wright State University.

Preface

When Thomas B. Rentschler, president of the Board of Directors of the Miami Conservancy District, met with us to discuss the publication of a pictorial history of the District, we knew only what thousands of people in the Miami Valley knew about the earthen dams in the valley:

That a terrible flood in 1913 had resulted in great loss of life and property and had led to the building of several protective dams in the valley.

Like thousands of other people here, we knew little more than that and lived our everyday lives in bland indifference to the endeavor that had raised up the massive piles of earth. Occasionally, we had a picnic at one of the parks around the dams or walked a trail around them, all the while giving virtually no thought to the past that had brought us here.

Then, as we examined the extensive collection of photographs that the District has reposited in the Archives and Special Collections at Wright State University, we became more and more conscious of, indeed astonished by, the magnitude and uniqueness of the great labor expended in the construction of the conservancy system.

Dependent wholly on local public support, the District had taken up the largest project of its kind in the nation and had turned labor, material and money into a sophisticated complex of dams and levees affording people in the Valley substantial protection against recurrence of a great flood.

What follows in words and pictures is a record and recreation of that endeavor. We urge readers to recollect these images as their everyday activities take them near the dams and levees that stand silently as sentinels for the security of the Miami Valley.

*   *   *

Anyone who takes up the task of research and writing knows or soon discovers that it is a cooperative, interdependent venture; he or she learns to look to the support of many other persons in the quest for sources and in learning more generally about the subject.

Certainly, that was the case in our venture. At the Archives and Special Collections of Wright State University, where the bulk of the photographs chronicling the flood and the construction of the conservancy system are housed, archivists gave us unstinting assistance. Particularly Dorothy Smith was ever ready to facilitate our use of them.

At the Miami Conservancy District, all the personnel always stood ready to help us in our search for relevant records. Donald Holtvoigt, manager of personnel/administration, had his door open at all times to hear our inquiries and requests.

At public and university libraries throughout the Miami Valley, librarians—those unsung heroes of research—gave generously of their time and services when we went to them for aid.

Though our debt to all these people is great, we must, of course, take responsibility for any errors of fact or interpretation that may have found their way into this book.

Carl M. Becker
Patrick B. Nolan
Dayton, Ohio, October 1987

Introduction

The forces of nature are both limitless and relentless. And although these forces control our lives, they are the source of never-ending beauty and fascination. No matter the season, we can be enthralled with a fresh snow, the green grass of summer, the brilliance of fall and the fresh, uplifting flowers and birds of springtime.

In our modern age we often seem able to defy the constraints that nature has imposed on human-kind since the beginning. Just a few generations ago we might have scoffed at the thought that coal or oil could be converted in some alchemical manner and hence transported to our homes and businesses via tiny wires to turn the night into day.

Or even more astounding, that we could go to the moon and return. For most of us, what nature does or does not do is taken for granted. Often our concern is no greater than whether we should wear a raincoat or wear wools instead of cottons.

We are all well aware, however, that the forces of nature are inexorable and unpredictable. Most of us have at least a passing understanding of the unusual and frequently horrifying phenomena that have occurred on our earth. They all seem to have names: avalanche, flood, pestilence, tidal wave, hurricane, tornado, lightning, and the list goes on.

Our environment is normally (whatever normal is) delightful. But occasionally, and unpredictably, one natural element builds up or comes into conflict with another to create conditions which may range from unpleasant to deadly.

Yet within one's lifetime, most of us never have a first-hand experience with such angry forces and thus may have a tendency to take them lightly, believing they occur elsewhere or in some other time. While it is true that most of nature's devastation is indeed limited to a few occasions and isolated geographically, the reality is that they have occurred, are occurring and will certainly occur again in the future.

This pictorial history of the Miami Conservancy District reveals to the residents of the Miami Valley and southwestern Ohio how powerful and devastating nature has been to us, and how we collectively have provided a large measure of protection against one of nature's most destructive forces: flood.

This book chronicles our valley's history of severe flooding. Since there has not been any recent noticeable flooding in any of the major metropolitan areas of the Miami Valley, there is a tendency to assume that the flood of 1913 was a one-time event. It was not, and the completed flood control system provides a major step beyond "flood insurance."

While insurance is designed to recoup loss following a catastrophic event, the Miami Conservancy District's flood control system is intended to prevent losses resulting from floods. The key to the theory of flood control in southwestern Ohio is prevention through protection.

While no one can guarantee that flooding will never again plague the Miami Valley, through foresight, planning and great care, the probability of another catastrophic flood has been immeasureably reduced.

Determined that the loss of life and property which devastated nine Miami Valley cities in 1913 was never to occur again, the area's citizens united to create the Miami Conservancy District. This is the first and only such protection anywhere locally conceived, engineered, funded, financed, maintained, managed and supported only by those who benefit from it.

The pages that follow are a pictorial history of the Miami Conservancy District. It is presented in an effort to graphically demonstrate the devastation that led to the construction of our flood control system, the recovery from the flood and the area's subsequent economic development. Though completed more than fifty years ago, many of these photographs are published for the first time.

Thomas B. Rentschler, President
Board of Directors
Miami Conservancy District

Nature is sometimes subdued
But seldom extinguished
Sir Francis Bacon (1561-1626)

Remember, Mother Nature bats last.

This aerial view of the Great Miami River and its principal tributaries in Dayton graphically demonstrates the river's determination, left to its own devices, to create its own channels. This photo shows the confluence with the Stillwater (upper left); the beginnings of Triangle and Island Parks and the abandoned McCook Field (upper center); the Mad River joining the Great Miami (upper right) and Wolf Creek flowing in from the northwest (middle left). This amazingly clear aerial photograph was taken in 1929 by Mayfield Aerial Surveys.

The Lay of the Land and Its History

Beginning in the 1780s and 1790s, the Americans of a new nation had entered the Miami Valley. A distinct physiographic region of more than five thousand square miles shaped by the Great Miami River and its principal tributaries, the Whitewater, Stillwater and Mad Rivers, it became the setting for the creation of a new society (Figure 1).

Here by treaty and war the pioneers had displaced the Miami, the Shawnee and the other Indians. Here they had cleared the forests and prepared the fields for farming, turning the valley into one the nation's great granaries. Here, too, they had laid out lots for communities that they envisioned as towns and cities—and the communities did indeed appear, among them Dayton, Hamilton, Middletown, Troy and Piqua. And here they began practicing the mechanical arts and pursuing commercial ventures.

The pioneers worked in a valley whose geological history had been characterized by cataclysmic change that prefigured, in a sense, a natural disaster. Perhaps 300,000,000 years ago a salt water sea covered most of the North American continent, including all of modern Ohio. As the sea gradually receded through a series of geological stages—the Cambrian period, the Ordovician period, and so on—land emerged in western Ohio and primitive forms of plant and animal life appeared.

Known among geologists as the Teays, a great river also eventually etched the new land, flowing from the Appalachian plateau across central Ohio. To the north its tributaries shaped uplands into hills and valleys; to the south they drained present Preble, Greene, Miami, Montgomery and Clark counties. The Teays and its tributaries represented the first real river system of the region.

Then a series of glacial movements formed new systems. The Kansas ice sheet, moving in from the west about 700,000 years ago, dammed the Teays and its tributaries and created a new drainage system. Depositing sediments in valleys, it laid the foundation for an underground water system that still serves the Miami Valley. Next, the Illinois ice sheet, perhaps 125,000 years ago, filled the streams with another glacial deposit of sand and gravel. Finally, the Wisconsin glacier, which swept over most of Ohio twenty thousand to thirty thousand years ago, created the present system (Figure 2).

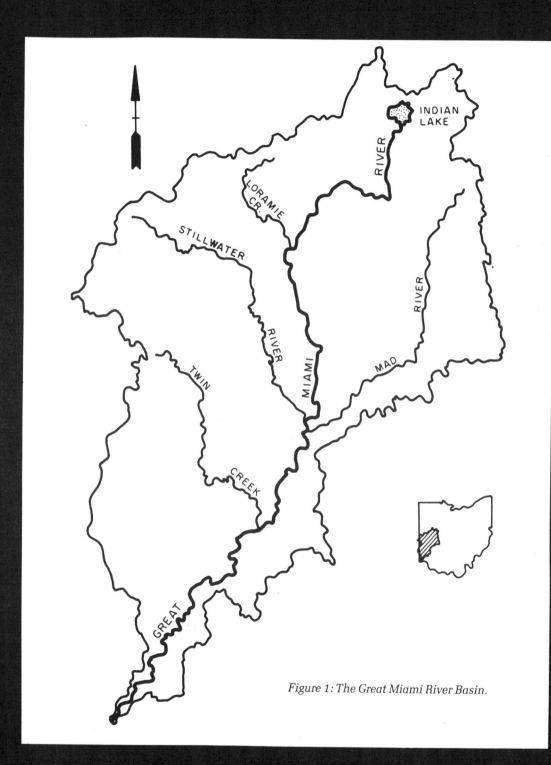

Figure 1: The Great Miami River Basin.

Together, the Wisconsin and earlier glaciers, pushing rock and soil into preglacial valleys, also provided great reservoirs of underground water. Even today Dayton lies over a buried valley four hundred feet deep that provides a fairly uniform flow of ground water. In western Hamilton County, permeable glacial deposits produce millions of gallons of water daily. Thus the great glaciers endowed generations of people with a bountiful land; unfortunately, though, they also left an environment vulnerable to a natural disaster, as a generation of the twentieth century would learn.

The pioneers coming into the territory, like founding settlers almost everywhere, first took up the most fertile lands adjacent to the waterways. Not only did these rivers and lakes assure abundant water they also provided the easiest transportation of people and produce and the energy to run mills.

The sons and daughters of the pioneer forefathers, caught up in the changes that they were making, gave scant attention to the origins of their new land. From the earliest days the valley's waterways were navigable mainly during the spring freshets. Providing a more dependable, though laborious, route of traffic were the rude country roads of the early nineteenth century which began to link the fledgling communities after the War of 1812. The southern portion of the Miami Canal, with all its promise as an easier mode of transport, crawled north through the valley in the 1820s and 1830s. By mid-century railroads began to crisscross the entire area.

All these modes of transportation served the agricultural life of the basin, and particularly the railroads promoted the rise of manufacturing in towns and cities. By the 1870s, Dayton had become a nationally important center for the production of railroad cars and agricultural implements and would soon host a great factory manufacturing cash registers for all corners of the globe—The National Cash Register Company (now NCR Corporation).

Hamilton also had many slings to its industrial bow. There the Niles Tool Works, a giant of its kind, was operating at mid-century; and the paper mills, sheet metal factories and grey iron foundries were at work. At Middletown paper mills were a common sight, and at the turn of the twentieth century, The American Rolling Mill Company (now ARMCO) began turning out steel for a far-flung market. Many decades earlier, entrepreneurs in Piqua were finding regional markets for their horseshoe bar iron, malleable iron and edged tools. Smaller communities were developing a wide array of production for local markets.

Population grew rapidly through the century in the principal counties comprising the basin. In the 1830s about 60,000 people lived in Butler, Montgomery and Miami counties; by 1910 the number had reached nearly 300,000.

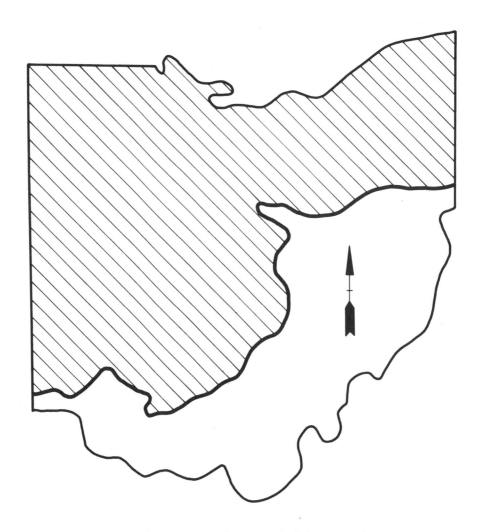

Figure 2: The Wisconsin Glacier reached deep into Ohio.

As their numbers grew and as they created economic vitality, the men and women of the Miami Valley established a variety of cultural and educational instruments. They organized public and private schools of all sorts: kindergartens, academies, normal schools, colleges. Of diverse national origins, they founded a multiplicity of churches. They raised up libraries, theaters and other institutions for edification and entertainment.

Living in an age when Americans set high store on the political crafts, people in the valley played an active role in local and national politics. They rallied to the national cause as disputes with Great Britain led to the War of 1812. They were participants in the democratization of political life in the 1820s and 1830s—the Jacksonian age. They took part in the acrimonious debate on slavery and the hotly- contested elections that opened the door to the Civil War; and young men from the valley fought and bled in the battles of that war. After the war, the people here vigorously argued the merits of prohibition, of regulating business, of women's rights, of returning to a bimetallic standard, and of many other issues. Along the way, they helped send seven Ohioans to the White House and countless others to important positions in Washington. They developed a tradition, so they believed, of local accomplishment and self-sufficiency.

Through the decades of growth, the people of the valley had faced only sporadic aberrations of an otherwise pleasant and benevolent nature. In 1811 they had felt the shaking edge of the great earthquake that had moved through the Ohio Valley. Though supposedly the vibrations did not entirely recede for a month, the fear of additional quakes soon passed. Tornadoes had occasionally struck the Miami Valley, but none in such force as to become fixed in the collective memory.

Floods had periodically visited the valley, most notably in 1805, 1828, 1847, 1866 and 1898. According to local tradition, the flood of 1805 brought eight feet of water into the streets of Dayton. That flood prompted the citizenry of Dayton and several communities along the Great Miami River to raise up earthen levees. After a flood, typically residents patched up river banks and strengthened levees. Following the flood of 1898, which nearly reached a record crest, communities in the valley began to consider more effective measures of flood control.

But there was no great sense of urgency, and no one had cut new channels in the river bed or built dams and new levees by the spring of 1913. The people living in the Great Miami River basin, seeing and sharing in the fruits of their forefathers' labor, were confident of their future; and the floods were but nuisances to be endured.

Flood covers a residential section near the Fairgrounds, Dayton (overleaf).

*This was Rossville on March 26, 1913 (below);
Rossville bridge an early casualty (above).*

Piqua's public square on March 26, 1913.

And the Waters Prevailed . . .

As winter turned to spring in March of 1913, at last the Wisconsin glacier brought the Miami Valley to an environmental rendezvous with destiny. That month saw three great air masses converging over the valley. One, developing in the Gulf of Mexico, came north with increasing speed; a second drifted south out of Canada; and a third, born over the Great Plains, gathered momentum on an eastward course toward Ohio.

At convergence, they delivered a Noah-like rainfall to the valley; from March 23 to March 27, nine to eleven inches of rain fell, an unprecedented amount for the area. The rain came at a particularly dangerous moment. Already the ice and snow of a hard winter had melted into the ground, and recent light rains had fallen; consequently, the already saturated ground could not accept much more moisture, and the water had to run into the creeks feeding the rivers of the valley. All together, nearly four trillion gallons of water, an amount equivalent to about thirty days' discharge of water over Niagara Falls, flowed through the Miami Valley during the ensuing flood.

What made the run-off more dangerous, especially for communities below Piqua and Troy, was the juncture of streams around Dayton. There the Great Miami became akin to a large tube that gradually diminished at its end. As the river passed through Dayton, taking on the flow of the Stillwater and Mad Rivers and Wolf Creek, its channel progressively narrowed—from eight hundred feet at the juncture of the Stillwater to five hundred feet at the southern edge of Dayton. The winding of the river into an 'S' aggravated the problem, exposing as it did, additional sections of the city to flooding. Altogether, certainly the waters could "prevail exceedingly upon the earth."

Though the communities in the upper Miami River basin did not stand at the mercy of the physiographic peculiarities facing Dayton, they became the first casualties of the Great Flood of 1913. At Piqua rain fell steadily all day Saturday and Sunday, March 22 and 23 and then came down in torrents on Monday. Residents there took no alarm when people in Rossville, a low-lying village near Piqua, had to leave their homes; it had happened before and would again, they believed.

Market Street in Troy under water.

People marooned in upper floors.

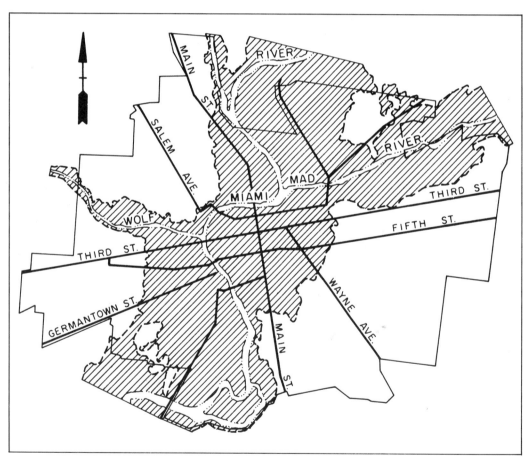

Figure 3: The flood in Dayton (shaded area) covered about 14 square miles.

Then on Monday, a levee in the northeast part of town broke despite repeated mending. A great volume of water surged through the gap and carried men, women and children and everything else before it, flooded the downtown, and inundated the eastern sections of the community. At Troy no levees broke; the water simply rose from the river and covered much of the town with what one observer called "a gigantic lake."

Dayton stood next in the route of the flood. There, as in Piqua, the citizenry had more curiosity than fear about consequences of a great rainfall. By Tuesday, though, water had backed up in the streets in the center of the city; and residents there and elsewhere became more apprehensive. Then the river, now completely out of control, overwhelmed the levees and sent new rivers into southern, eastern and western parts of the city. Eventually, the flood covered about fourteen square miles there (Figure 3).

To the south, the river also had its way. A thousand residents of Middletown fled their homes as waters came into their streets. At Hamilton the river rushed over its banks on Tuesday and soon flooded the Third and Fifth Wards there, and then spread three miles from the Erie Highway on the east side to D Street on the west side. Flood waters also found their way into smaller communities throughout the valley: Franklin, Miamisburg, Germantown and West Carrollton, among others. Inevitably, too, the flood reached into rural areas.

Everywhere the flood brought disaster. Rising rapidly, it drove people to seek shelter in trees, on roofs and in attics where they awaited rescue. Rushing torrentially, the waters swept away bridges, dwellings and commercial buildings— and anyone who was in them. It precipitated fires at broken gas mains, which spread when fed by spilled gasoline. In Dayton, a fire erupted at a drug store, consumed nearly two blocks of business buildings and threatened for a time to fan out in all directions. At Hamilton, within two hours the flood swept away three of the four bridges there and claimed the fourth a few hours later.

The Great Miami River 27 feet above low water mark, taken from Dayton View Heights, March 26, 1913 at 10:30 a.m.; West Monument Avenue (above).

Horses seek safer ground near Fourth and
Ludlow Streets (above); looking east on Fourth
Street (right).

Near the high water mark in Dayton; looking west from NCR, Edgemont and Stewart Street bridges are gone (left); Fourth Street looking west from Ludlow (above); looking north from Fairgrounds hill, corner of Apple and Ludlow Streets (below).

Crowds gathered at water's edge, looking southeast from the corner of Cornell and Summit Streets, CH&D RR embankment in foreground (right, above); Fifth Street west from Clinton Street (below).

Common sights during flood in Dayton: Burns Avenue (right); Warren Street looking north from Brown Street (middle); north end of Dayton View bridge looking toward downtown (below).

Lifeline rigged on Burns Avenue (above); swift current on Eagle Street (left); corner of Second and Webb Streets in East Dayton (left, below).

Trio of postcards show downtown Dayton flood scenes.

Another view from Fairgrounds hill, taken from Main Street with Apple Street in foreground.

Mad River looking northwest near East Monument Avenue between Keowee and Findlay Streets (top); railroad tracks under water on the west side (center); Broadway at Wolf Creek (right).

Main Street looking south from Fifth Street (above); West Third Street from Third and Main (below). Note crowd on fire escape at extreme left, Arcade near center of picture.

The flood at Hamilton also was severe: the Republican News building on North Third Street (above) and a horse struggles against the current downtown (below). Pictures taken on March 25, 1913.

Water almost covers street lights (upper); the bridge at High and Main Streets, Hamilton, about to go down (left and below). Cameraman C. S. Jacobi took this remarkable sequence as the massive steel structure was falling.

HIGH AND MAIN STREET BRIDGE BEFORE THE FLOOD.

THE FALL OF THE BRIDGES

Black street bridge went down Tuesday, March 25, at 12:12 P. M.

High street bridge went down Tuesday, March 25, at 12:28 P. M.

C., H. & D. railroad bridge went down Tuesday, March 25, at 2:12 P. M.

Columbia bridge went down Wednesday, March 26, at 2:15 A. M.

Total cost of the three bridges $240,000. They can not be replaced today for less than $300,000.

The "Fall of the Bridges" in Hamilton (left); a swift current, six feet at its crest, rushed down the middle of Main Street.

Force of the river, carrying tons of logs and other debris, about to destroy the bridge (above); High Street, Hamilton, at daybreak on March 26, 1913 (below).

FLOOD EXTRA

DAYTON DAILY NEWS

FLOOD EXTRA

Issued from the Offices of The National Cash Register Company, Dayton, Ohio

VOL. XXVII. No. 185. DAYTON, OHIO, FRIDAY, MARCH 28, 1913

DAYTON FACING SITUATION WITH WONDERFUL BRAVERY

Flood Victims of Every Section of the Stricken City Being Provided For as Rapidly as Possible. The Aged and Infants Come First In the Rescue Work. Churches, Schools and Public Buildings are Turned Into Hospitals. Militia Has the City Well in Hand and the Relief Work Has Been Wonderfully Systemized. Plans Already Devised For the Restoration of Dayton.

With clearing skies and warmer temperature, with the water rapidly receding and the streets cleared sufficiently to permit of free passage from all parts of the city people began to take heart and conditions were better than they had been at any time since the floods came.

The work of rescue was going forward rapidly in all parts of the city. It had been taking place from every available point leading to higher ground from the beginning of the high water, but as the water receded it went forward with greater rapidity.

Every chool honse and every church outside the flooded district was utilized as a relief headquarters and as a place of refuge. At first surprisingly few were brought in, owing to the danger of going out into the mad current with the few boats at hand. By Thursday night the business district was cleared of most of those persons who wished to leave. There was still a large amount of water left in the district immediately east of the river, along Second, Third, Fourth and Fifth streets, but went down so rapidly Friday morning that it was not long until all were out who wished to leave.

Those who came out Friday morning were in bad conditions. Every face showed the traces of the terrible suspense and suffering. The lack of water to drink caused the greatest suffering, and the cold had been intense in the weakened condition of the survivors.

Worst of all the suffering was the mental agony through which all passed during the long imprisonment. First it was the flood, creeping up inch by inch, until Tuesday midnight. Thousands, driven gradually from first to second floor, at attic and to roofs, were in the depths of despair as there seemed to be no hope of escape.

Rev. Father Bernard O'Reilly, president of St. Mary's Institute, said Friday afternoon that 520 people are being taken care of at S. M. I. All are in good health there, he said, and are receiving ample rations and attentions. Because of the fact that all the boarding students were away on their Easter vacations when the floo dstruck the city, the sufferers were afforded better comforts and more room than under ordinary circumstances. The boys dormitories, class rooms and the huge gymnasium were turned into sleeping quarters and besides the provisions which came in by rail, the S. M. I. received many wagon loads of foods from farmers in the country.

It was announced by Father O'Reilly that the school will be closed indefinitely for day scholars, as well as for boarding students.

(Probably no more dramatic incidents were witnessed during the appalling hours of Tuesday afternoon and night than those which occurred at Main and Foraker Ave. following the explosion near Saettle's grocery at Main and Vine streets. Men and women, failing to make their cries heard by rescuers or thrown out upon the rushing waters by the toppling over of their homes, grasped hold of the telegraph poles and made their way to the heavy cable above. In the sight of a great throng on the fair grounds hill, these people made their way along the cable until they came close enough to shore to be grasped by willing hands and carried to safety.)

(Horrors multiplied and grew when the cry of "run for the hills" was heard broadcast Thursday morning. Believing that their homes were to be washed away and they would be confronted with the same fate which overtook their townsmen below, the people of the South Park, from Hickory street south and all through the residential section, fled pell-mell from their home and took to the Schantz Plat and to the hills of Woodland Cemetery.

Placards and posters, hurriedly printed by hand at the N. C. R. and spread around at points of vantage, reassured the fleeing populace and they were persuaded to return to their homes within a few hours.)

Edward Morgenthaler, Warren and Vine streets, died just as rescuers were reaching out for him. His heart weakened by the exposure and shock, Morgenthaler dropped back dead into the water as he was about to be assisted from his home into a boat.

The shrieks from those who thought themselves trapped by the water caused the most intense suffering even in those whose situation was least terrifying. Later the fear of fire added to the distress of those who were unable to escape through the water.

Friday morning the city was full of soldiers. The militia was reinforced at all points by the soldiers of the U. S. army, and there seemed to be ample protection for the city at all points. Martial law practically prevails, and no persons are permitted to pass to and from the flooded district without permits from the military authorities which are carefully scrutinized.

Sanitation is the big problem. With care on the part of everybody, and quick, organized work, sickness may be avoided, impossible as it now seems.

Adjutant General's Orders

Adjutant-General Wood has ordered that all persons dig holes in their yards into which must be poured all slop water, offal and garbage. Throw nothing into the streets or yards. Bury everything. As soon as the sun comes out all matter will decay and render life hazardous in the city unless the Adjutant-General's orders are compiled with.

DAYTON CITY UNDERTAKERS

MR. J. H. PATTERSON wants to meet you at the Office Building of the N. C. R. Co. this evening at 8 o'clock.

All Guests At Rotterman Safe

The guests at the Rotterman apartment, Third and Ludlow streets, had thrilling experiences, but all are safe.

The building caught fire and it looked for a time that the occupants would have to jump into the raging waters but they ascended to the roof and by the aid of planks crossed to the Atlas Hotel.

From this point they gave the flames battle and succeeded in extinguishing them. Mr. Rotterman's head was split open and, while the wound is quite serious, his recovery is assured by those in attendance.

Among the guests were: Mr. and Mrs. Rennick, Dayton, Mr. and Mrs. Albert Swope of Springfield; Mr. and Mrs. Enrst, Dayton; Mr. and Mrs. Odea of Helena, Montana; H. C. Washington of Goderich, Ontario.

Jensen, Harrisan and Woodward are also safe.

The guests report that three buildings in Main Street, between Thirl and Fourth Streets, collapsed. The guests suffered from thirst and hunger but they remained cool and brave.

Young Lad Doing

George Houck, the 13-year-old son of Mr. and Mrs. Thurston Houck of Oakwood, is probably the youngest lad engaged in the relief work.

Since Tuesday morning he has been busy carrying supplies to the sufferers in his own, canoe and brave men have trembled as they watched him glide over the water.

His principal aim has been to get milk and food to families, saving babies.

Stay at Home.

Those who live in the districts not flooded should remain at home unless it is absolutely necessary to leave. This will greatly faciliate the work of rescue and relief.

Engineer Appointed

H. E. Talbot, Prominent Dayton Citizen, Selected to Have Charge of All Construction Work.

General Wood to-day issued the following order:

Headquarters Ohio National Guard.

March 28, 1913.

H. E. Talbot is hereby appointed Chief Engineering Officer of this District.

He will have charge of road construction, repair work, engineering, undertaking, etc.

His orders will be obeyed by the O. N. G.

(Signed) James M. Cox, Governor, by Geo. H. Wood, Adj. Gen.

This will be reassuring news to the people of Dayton, since Mr. Talbot is so well known here as an able expert in construction work. He has accepted his new office, and will begin at once cleaning the streets and sewers, and pjerfecting his plans for a general remodeling of such public works as have been damaged by the flood.

It is believed that Mr. Talbot's selection of this important position will be the beginning of the solution of Dayton's water trouble. He has already stated that he believes it to be possible to so contsruct levees and broaden and deepen the channel of the river as to render it probably certain that no overflow will again damage the city.

Situation Looks Much Brighter

The situation looks much brighter this morning, the rain and snow having ceased, and the sun is shining brightly. Telegraph service is being restored and relief trains on D L & C are bringing in large quantities of supplies, etc.

Reports from North Dayton are very favorable, there being little suffering and the loss of life is estimated at a low figure. Transportation is not yet opened up to any extent.

The N C R Company is doing admirable relief work and have the situation well in hand. Water is receding from the business section, and active relief work is being carried on there.

No fires are reported at this writing. A fair estimate of the total number of lives lost cannot be given for some time to come. Relief is being given to the people on the North Side of the city. Relief work is being hindered to some extent by crowds of curious people.

The Cold a Blessing

The citizens should not complain of the cold weather. It is the salvation here and it is the earnest request of the committee in charge that the people be brave and remember that the cold snap is just what it needed, although it may cause suffering, until the flood situation is righted.

U. S. Life Saving Crew

The U. S. life saving crew, stationed at Louisville, reached Dayton yesterday afternoon, and immediately began the work of rescuing the citizens from their homes.

The crew has kept at their task constantly since its arrival and has performed yeoman service.

The Citizens' Committee

Full Authority to Act in Behalf of the People of Dayton Conferred Upon President Patterson

Governor Cox Wires His Approval of the Selection of the President and Will Order the National Guard to Comply With All Demands Of The Committee.

OHIO NATIONAL GUARD HEADQUARTERS

Dayton, Ohio, March 28, 1913.

Mr. John H. Patterson, President of The National Cash Register Company, is hereby appointed President of the Citizens' Relief Committee.

All orders signed by him will be honored by all posts of the National Guard.

By order of Governor James M. Cox.

GEO. H. WOOD, Adjutant General.

(At a meeting of a number of citizens Thursday, a Citizens' Committee was organized, and President John H. Patterson elected President, with W. F. Bippus, Secretary and Treasurer. Full authority was granted the President to act for and in behalf of the Committee in all matters pertaining to the welfare of Dayton.

Governor Cox immediately notified the militia of President Patterson's selection, and ordered it to comply fully with the general policy outlined by the Committee.

It will be the duty of this Committee to take entire charge of the relief work for the present and the future upbuilding of the city. It will accept and receipt for all donations of supplies and money, however they may be sent to this city.)

It is only through the systematic work of such a committee that Dayton can hope to recover from the terrible blow which she received. But all persons in this city know what is means to have such a man as President Patterson at the helm with full power to devise systems and methods. It means that stricken Dayton will emerge from this calamity a bigger, a brighter and a better city in which to live and to do business.

President Patterson will, of course, co-operate with all other civic bodies to the end that the greatest relief may be afforded for the present and the most splendid plan worked out for the future. The citizens of Dayton can do no less than to at once lend to the Citizens' Committee every means within their power to further this needful work.

IMMENSE LOSS

To mercantile stocks in downtown district. All basement and first floor goods ruined.

The downtown district of Dayton is a place indescribable. Save for the fires, there have been few buildings apparently ruined. The magnificent steel high school has a great hole in the front, maybe fifty feet wide and three stories high. It stands close to the river and may be entirely undermined. The condition of other buildings seems to be safe, but nothing is known.

Persons familiar with the business district will form some conception by being told that there is not a store which has escaped. Magnificent department stores are in horrible conditiond. The muddy flood swirled nearly t othe ceiling of every first floor. Everything that would float has been overturned and reduced to worthless debris. That tells the story of every store big and little.

Thomas Elder of the Elder and Johnston Company said Friday morning that he had little idea of the loss in his store.

"It will not be less than $250,000,' he said.

Lime Catches Fire And People Jump

They Prefer to Take Chance with Water and are Saved.

(Mr. Hart of Huffman Avenue, freight agent for the Penn. lines had one of the most thrilling escapes, reported He and several other officials of the road were in the yards when the water poured down on them

They scrambled into the first car, which they were able to reach. It happened to contain considerable lime. The water reached the lime finally and it caught fire.

Mr. Hart and his companions were in great danger of being burned to death, if they remained. There was only one alternative and that was to leap into the raging waters and take a chance of reaching another car. This they did and they were successful. They climbed to the top and remained there for 48 hours before being rescued.)

Warning

The occupant of every house is required to build a cess-pool in the back yard, sufficient large to hold the excreta.

John H Patterson

Aide in Charge of the Southern Military District of Dayton

The March 28, 1913 edition was "issued from the offices of the National Cash Register Company."

Rescuers bring people to safety; note high water marks on buildings (overleaf).

Balm in Gilead: Rescue, Relief and Recovery

By and large, rescuers acted independently with little direction and with whatever equipment they could muster to save people. Owning or commandeering skiffs and rowboats, men rowed through streets looking for people stranded by the flood waters. Sometimes the rescuers lost their lives when surging currents overturned their boats or carried wreckage into them. Sometimes, of course, individuals improvised means of saving themselves.

Fittingly enough, in Dayton, a center of manufacturing, the NCR, the leading factory of the city and a model of industrial efficiency, became a model of efficiency in rescue efforts. Well-known for his vigorous and sometimes eccentric direction of the company, president John H. Patterson put his carpenters to work building boats and dispatched rescue crews to the flooded streets. Altogether, rescuers in boats took at least ten thousand men, women and children from perches of refuge, eight thousand in Dayton alone.

From almost the first day of the flood, stories of tragedy, suffering, heroism and selfishness became the stuff of lore. People in Piqua long recalled Clarence White for his derring-do rescues of people from trees and roofs. He saved an old man in Rossville, a Job-like man who had remained in a tree for sixty hours awaiting rescue, all the while singing hymns to sustain his spirit. Richard Bateman, a 57-year-old man, rowed his boat around Piqua for thirty miles through driftwood, roofs and parts of bridges to rescue one hundred people; he received a Carnegie Medal of Honor for his valor. C. B. Jamison, a prominent Piqua attorney, lost his life in a magnificent effort to save a woman and her child from the rushing waters.

At Dayton and other communities, one could hear for years similar accounts of heroism and tragedy. Despite efforts to save him from a floating roof on Main Street, an old man sank into the surging water when the roof fell apart. A husband and wife saved themselves and their child by slowly hitching along telephone wires until they reached dry ground. One intrepid rescuer used the oars of his boat to seek out and recover a baby who had been sucked under the water by a whirlpool.

Crawling to safety along telephone wires, Dayton.

This family rescued itself with boat built in attic.

It was still raining when rescue efforts began. Here an NCR-built boat is met at flood's edge (above), rowboat brings others to shore (below).

Company E of the Ohio National Guard performed numerous missions of mercy at Hamilton.

Unfortunately, in nearly every community a tale of selfishness surfaced. In one instance, a man refused rescue crews use of his boat; elsewhere profiteers attempted to exact high prices. Heroism notwithstanding, when the waters receded, they had taken a terrible toll: more than three hundred people had perished and property damage exceeded $100,000,000. As many as 123 people died in Dayton and the surrounding area; at least one thousand houses were destroyed.

But losses in other communities were even higher proportionally. In Hamilton 106 people lost their lives, more than five hundred houses were washed away, and one factory incurred damages of more than $2,000,000. In Piqua no less than forty-nine people drowned; at Troy fourteen perished.

Relief for victims of the flood came from many sources. Though often improvised, unlike the efforts at rescue it took on a degree of coherency, rational organization and the use of new technology that one would expect in an age that took increasing pride in centralization and mechanization of power.

In nearly every community, people whose homes had escaped the flood opened their doors to families needing food and shelter. A family in Middletown sheltered seventeen people for several days, and a woman in Miamisburg turned her home into a relief station. Citizens' relief committees appeared in virtually every stricken community. At Piqua the Business Men's Association, the Young Men's Christian Association and citizens generally cooperated in establishing relief stations where those needing help could secure food and clothing. The agent in charge of the Pennsylvania Railroad sent two engines and cars into the countryside foraging for provisions.

Using the slogan "Troy will take care of her own," a citizens' relief committee there canvassed the community for subscriptions to a relief fund and soon raised more than $10,000.

Couple awaits rescue on porch roof near Fourth and Washington Streets (left); loaded rowboat makes its solitary way from Williams Street bridge over Wolf Creek (above).

Scenes like these were common during the 1913 flood. Rescuers help woman walk the plank to safety (right); man and woman cling to improvised raft in Hamilton (below).

A COMMON SIGHT DURING FLOOD
MAN & WOMAN ON RAFT
SOUTH MONUMENT AVE, MARCH 25, 1913.
HAMILTON OHIO.

At Dayton relief took on a more variegated nature. In Dayton View, a northern section of the city, residents established temporary relief stations. Churches and fraternal organizations on the east side gave succor to the afflicted. But the most notable aspect of relief here came at "The Cash." Patterson, who had three trains sent from New York City with supplies, turned the facilities of his factory to a vast program of relief; here his work force, numbering about seven thousand, constituted a great relief force. Here, thousands of people received food, clothing and shelter—and even the small amenities of life—haircuts, shoeshines, and so forth. Dayton also saw the National Guard, which had been called in to enforce martial law, extending measures of relief.

In Middletown and Hamilton, relief committees offered assistance to those driven from their homes by the flood. Probably Hamilton was the first city in the basin to receive outside help when a citizens' relief committee in Cincinnati sent medical supplies and boats. Later that committee dispatched nurses, physicians and social workers to Dayton, Middletown, Miamisburg and Hamilton. Ultimately, the American Red Cross assumed control of relief in all the flooded communities.

As the flood waters receded and as the urgency of relief lessened, the communities of the flood began to look to recovery. Various agencies participated in effecting the return to normal patterns of life. Authorities of the National Guard administered emergency government in several communities, notably Dayton and Hamilton, that for more than a month maintained law and order before returning the government to civil authorities.

More survivors arriving in hastily-built NCR boat.

Initially, citizens' relief committees took up the task of physically rehabilitating communities. But in Dayton and other cities, eventually at the request of Ohio Governor James M. Cox of Dayton, sanitary officers of the United States Army assumed that duty. A key figure was Major Thomas Rhoads, under whose direction soldiers and civilians managed the restoration of sewerage, water and gas services. An odious but necessary task was the removal of animal carcasses from streets and houses. Nearly 1500 horses drowned in Dayton. Post cards appeared in the wake of the flood showing horses dead in grotesque positions. The Bicycle Club in Dayton, acting in cooperation with sanitary officials, hauled large animals to an incinerating plant outside the city. Countless domestic animals also had to be removed.

The receding flood also left tons of mud and debris. Additionally, because many homes did not have direct connections to sewer lines or regular garbage pickup, the water released the contents of outhouses, cesspools and garbage pits creating a health hazard. Sanitary officials saw to the removal of this material by impressing private wagons and trucks. The NCR in Dayton and ARMCO in Middletown made switching or dummy locomotives capable of running on streetcar tracks available to haul away the flotsam and jetsam of the flood. The sanitary people had to devise numerous measures, too, for limiting the spread of contagious diseases, the creation of temporary morgues, the return to marketing, the reopening of schools and much more.

By early May, life in the valley had returned to a semblance of normalcy; but disaster and tragedy were becoming the agents for a new kind of life there.

Thousands of people were rescued in these flat-bottomed boats turned out in a hurry at NCR (upper, left); two men could take these boats virtually anywhere there was even a little water (right); a few more steps to drier land (bottom, left).

Though relief for flood victims came from various quarters, only the relief program at NCR had its history chronicled in photographs. Here, thousands formed long lines (left) for all sorts of relief services offered at The Cash.

John H. Patterson (left, in derby) gave over the facilities of his factory and his work force to help the refugees. Here people could find food and shelter, medical help, seek missing relatives and friends; there was even barber and bootblack service.

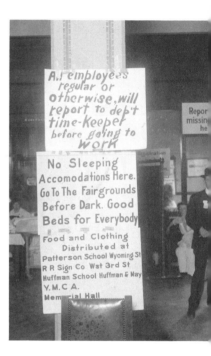

All employees regular or otherwise, will report to dep't time-Keeper before going to work

No Sleeping Accomodations Here. Go To The Fairgrounds Before Dark. Good Beds for Everybody

Food and Clothing Distributed at Patterson School Wyoming St R R Sign Co Wst 3rd St Huffman School Huffman & May Y.M.C.A. Memorial Hall

Repor missing he

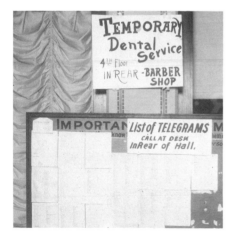

TEMPORARY Dental Service 4th Floor IN REAR BARBER SHOP

IMPORTAN List of TELEGRAMS CALL AT DESK InRear of Hall.

CLOTHES cleaned & pressed ALL NIGHT Service No Pay No Tips

Barber Shop 4th Floor rear Open all hours Day & Night No Pay No Tips.

Report and Return all articles Lost or Found to Police Headquarters.

Boot-Black Service Free

All N.C.R. Employes sleeping in building report at Dr. Herman's Office

Leave all information concerning any blind person in Dayton at nurses Headquarters

50

PUBLIC COMFORT STATION.

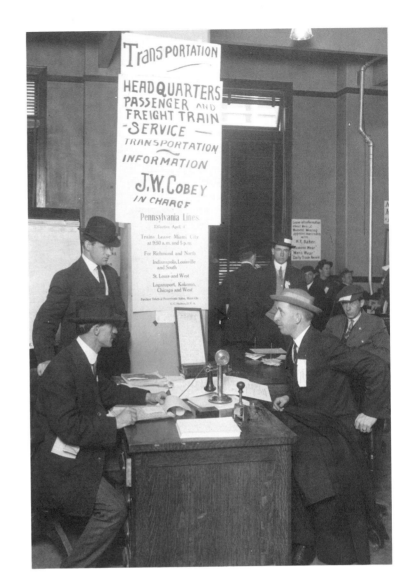

Even as people stood in line for food and other relief services (left, center and bottom), the National Guard set up a tent city for the homeless on NCR grounds. Below, Guardsmen at their cook tent.

AFTER THE FLOOD: Once the waters receded and the fires burned out, people throughout the valley could behold the scenes of death and destruction. Bodies of the dead in make-shift morgues awaited identification. Horses (more than one thousand drowned in Dayton) and other animals lay in grotesque patterns in the streets. Houses pushed off their foundations tilted precariously and awkwardly awaiting a final fall. Commercial and factory buildings were piled with debris left by the onrush of water through them. Bridges tumbled into the streams they had once spanned. And fertile soil, only recently readied for spring planting, washed away leaving a scarred crust of rock and mud.

Scenes of destruction: Union Station (upper left); clean up begins near East Third and Jefferson Streets (bottom, left); someone's pride and joy upended on Robert Boulevard (above); monumental clean up job on Maple Street (right).

All that remained of railroad bridge in Dayton (upper left); Ludlow Street appears relatively unharmed (bottom left); streetcar ended up on Monument Avenue in front of badly-damaged Steele High School (above); debris collected at bridges (below).

The beautiful Main Street bridge held but suffered damage (upper left); the Barney and Smith car works were hit so hard (left) they shortly went out of business; all that was left of the Fifth Street bridge in Dayton (above); utter desolation at the site of Webster Street bridge over the Mad River (right).

A great deal of expensive machinery was destroyed or seriously damaged. This had been the press room at the Dayton Paper Novelty Company (above); workers watch helplessly as waters rise at Barney and Smith (right).

Mud was deposited everywhere by the receding waters. This is in the Delco plant (above); at left, employees of the Teutonia Insurance Company dry papers on April 9, 1913.

OFFICE
TEUTONIA INS. CO.
RESULT OF FLOOD
MARCH - 25 - 1913
TAKEN APRIL - 9TH - 1913

Dead horses were one of the immediate public health problems (above); interior of paper warehouse (right); Requarth's lumber yard on Monument Avenue (below).

Residents of Wilkinson Street survey the damage between Fourth and Fifth Streets (left); making plans at the southeast corner of Third and Jefferson Streets (below).

Fifth Street, looking west from Wayne Avenue; Raper M.E. church on right.

Riverdale west of Main Street.

Only the water moved!

Battered levee on west bank of Great Miami River looking south from below Third Street bridge. Clean up has started, laundry out to dry.

A staggering clean up task
faced Dayton neighborhoods
hit hard by the flood. Note
holes cut in eaves and roofs
(bottom, center) by some
who escaped.

The flood trapped this street car on East Fifth Street near La Belle (top); only the cash register remained upright in Seattle's Grocery store (above). The north side of Fifth Street west of Wilkinson Street was almost totally destroyed (upper right); houses in some Dayton neighborhoods were floated off their foundations (right).

In North Dayton, the levee below the Herman Avenue bridge (above) was piled high with houses; other examples of houses which, like Humpty Dumpty, could not be put together again. These scenes are from various parts of Dayton.

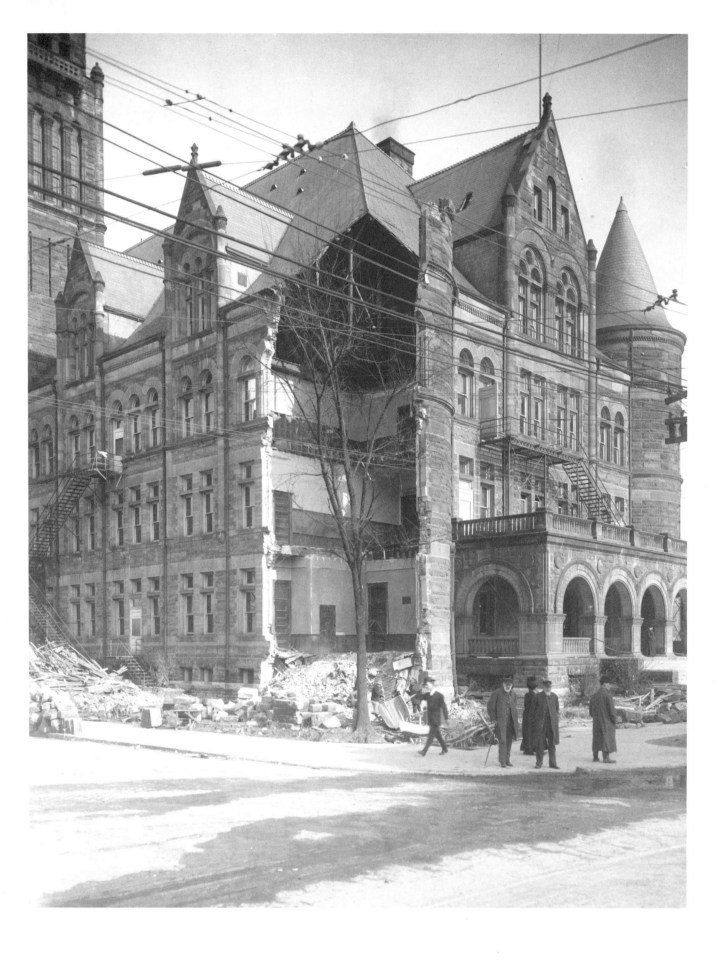

Swirling waters ripped off one of Steele High School's round towers (left); and did considerable damage to the Masonic Tample on South Main Street between Fourth and Fifth Streets (right). Bodies in a temporary morgue await burial (below).

Fires, started as a result of ruptured gas mains, also added to the destruction. Here are the remains of the Jewel Theater at the southwest corner of Third and Jefferson Streets (above and below) and Schoenberger's Drug store at the northwest corner of Fifth and Wilkinson Streets (right). A church at the northwest corner of Third and St. Clair Streets (far right) was destroyed while only the chimneys and fences remained here (bottom right).

In Hamilton, some streets were almost obliterated. The pavement of Vine Street (right) was buried under debris. Many other streets in Hamilton also suffered serious damage. A wrecked railroad car reclines on the river bank (below, right).

The Backus home on High Street in
Hamilton (above) was a complete
wreck; debris was piled high as the
second floor on Hanover Street (left);
and this is the scene that greeted
molders as they returned to work at
the Rentschler foundry (below).

Downtown Hamilton damage was extensive also. Here's a view of
High Street, looking west from Fifth Street, with the Soldiers' and
Sailors' Monument in the distance (above). Main Street, from the river,
gives an idea of the force of the current (below).

East Abutment of Great Bridge, Flood at Hamilton, Ohio

A picture postcard history of the 1913 flood at Hamilton.

South B Street from Main. Flood at Hamilton, Ohio

City Hall, North Monument Ave., Flood at Hamilton, Ohio

Ruins of C. H. & D. R. R. Bridge Across Great Miami River, and Near Completion of Temporary Bridge.   Flood, March 25, 1913, Hamilton, Ohio.

COLUMBIA CARRIAGE WORKS HAMILTON, OHIO. FLOOD

Life began returning to normal as soon as the flood waters
started to recede. While one horse is hitched to a wagon
another is still on its own (above); women returning from
market (below).

Scenes of destruction would be a constant reminder to people in Hamilton of the fury of the flood waters.

Middletown's Clark Street is under water (above), so is Charles Street (upper center) and its Jefferson school, which is still standing there. Steam engine and flat cars were used to haul away debris from downtown Middletown (below).

In Middletown, before 6:30 a.m. on March 26, 1913, Cincinnati police
help with the rescue effort: at Fourth and Curtis Streets (above);
launching boats (below).

(Photos on these two pages from the Middletown Public Library.)

Communities to the north suffered extensive damage also. In Piqua, an abandoned auto sits on West High (above); residents survey damage to Shawnee bridge (below); flood-moved houses on North Main Street (top right); heavily damaged house on East Water Street in Troy (bottom right).

There was no way around it. The wreckage, the mud, was there, everywhere; and it had to go if communities were to survive and flourish again. By pick-ax, shovel and rake, men, women and children piled up the debris. Then by wagons, trucks and flatcars pulled by small engines, they removed it and buried it at dumps.

In Springfield, the force of the water tore high holes in the underpinnings of the Beckel Avenue bridge (left); close up of the damage (top left); many homes were damaged (above).

But the flood was far from an urban problem only as fields all over the Miami Valley lost top soil or were covered by gravel and rocks. Farmers were left with a lot of reclamation work to make their fields fertile again.

The clean-up and cheer-up; workmen at Koors on Fifth Street near Ludlow (upper left); the Elder & Johnston Company, now Elder-Beerman, reopened its store on Main Street between Fourth and Fifth Streets (right).

As businesses struggled to reopen, the clean-up continued. Hosing down Ludlow Street near Fourth Street (upper left); repairing damage at Rike's (lower left); mud still covers West Third Street (above); typical scene on Fifth Street between Main and Jefferson Streets (left).

THE M.D. LARKIN SUPPLY CO.
NEW LOCATION 116 N. MAIN ST. BELL PHONE MAIN 275

A shovel brigade goes to work on Third Street (left) while a hard-hit business gets ready to move (above); 1100 block on West Third Street (below).

The clean-up crews faced an enormous task; removing mud in the neighborhoods (far left, top and below); pick up sticks in the lumber yard (bottom left).

All kinds of rolling stock was pressed into service for the clean up: the NCR locomotive (top, right) on South Main Street; flat cars on West Third Street (bottom, right); horse-drawn wagons on Burns Avenue (above); and the Delco Reconstruction and Relief brigade (below). The car (right) remains after the garage floated away. The locomotive is at Carillon Park.

"ALL THE PEOPLE OF THE MIAMI VALLEY REGARDLESS OF PERSONAL INTEREST OR LOCATION SHOULD STRIVE FOR THE COMMON GOOD OF THE ENTIRE VALLEY.
LET THE CITIZENS LABOR STEADFASTLY AND DEVOTEDLY FOR THE VALLEY AS A WHOLE, IN CO-OPERATION WITH EACH OTHER, RECOGNIZING THAT WHAT IS GOOD FOR ONE IS GOOD FOR THE OTHER, AND NEVER LOSING SIGHT OF THE FACT THAT THE FUTURE OF THE GREAT OHIO VALLEY LIES IN THE HANDS OF ALL OF US, NOT WITHIN THE GRASP OF ANY SELECTIVE FEW OR ANY CERTAIN COMMUNITY—
— E.A.DEEDS —

MAKE MIAMI VALLEY MIGHTY

The campaign for creation of the Conservancy District was a compendium of warnings, promises, mass rallies and legal maneuvering that the Miami Valley had never experienced before. It brought people into conflict, especially farmers in the northern areas of the valley against urban residents to the south; but the majority willed finally for the construction of dams to protect the valley.

DELAYING THE RESCUE

The $2,000,000-goal was reached by the end of May through rallies such as this one (overleaf). Newspaper cartoons also show support for a Conservancy District.

THE LOBBY BACK OF THE FLOOD CONSERVANCY ACT

Make Miami Valley Mighty

Though of necessity the residents of the basin gave their essential attention to survival in the days immediately following the flood, they soon began to consider and take steps toward protecting themselves and their property against another deluge. In April of 1913, at the request of local leaders and Gov. Cox, Ohio's General Assembly enacted legislation authorizing municipalities to establish emergency commissions to initiate appropriate measures for flood control.

In response, Hamilton and Middletown joined in creating such a commission, and citizens in Troy called on several other cities to join in a cooperative venture to discipline the streams around them. Particularly, they called on John H. Patterson to lead their effort. Representatives from ten counties organized The Miami Valley Flood Prevention Association, but nothing came of their efforts; and ultimately Dayton took the lead in forwarding a program for flood control.

Patterson was instrumental in organizing a flood prevention committee in Dayton, which, employing the slogan, "Remember the promises you made in the attic," raised $2,000,000 by the end of May to initiate planning for a system of flood control. Without delay, the committee engaged the Morgan Engineering Company of Memphis, Tennessee to take up that task.

Arthur E. Morgan, the principal partner in the company, had already won national repute as a creative engineer for his flood control and drainage projects in the lower Mississippi Valley.

From the outset, Morgan resolved to prepare a comprehensive plan, insisting that he could not use half-completed ideas for the sake of satisfying public demands that the dirt start flying. Nonetheless, he moved vigorously.

Early in June he had fifty men organized into surveying parties for preparing a topographic survey of the Great Miami River flood plain. Unfortunately, United States Geological Survey topographical maps were available for only a few parts of the Miami Valley. Years later, in 1951, Morgan noted that had they been published for the entire valley, six engineers working at their desks could have completed the survey in a few weeks. Instead, Morgan's crew tramped around the countryside "dressed like cowboys," as one observer complained, and took about two months to complete the surveys.

John H. Patterson

E. A. Deeds

Arthur Morgan

By October of 1913, Morgan had in hand a preliminary report setting forth eight alternative and sometimes interrelated plans for flood control. Ultimately, in one way or another, five of the eight proposals found their way into the final plan for creation of a system of levees and dams in the valley. The three proving unfeasible proposed diversion of the Great Miami, the Mad and the Stillwater Rivers into new channels around Dayton.

The remaining proposals called for improvement and straightening of river channels in Dayton and attendant changes in bridges spanning them, raising levees there, and construction of four storage reservoirs to contain flood waters. Estimated cost was $12,000,000. That figure, however, did not take into account extensive channel improvements at Hamilton and of a dam and reservoir near Germantown. Cost of all reservoirs, dams and local improvements, fueled by a war-induced inflation, ultimately came to more than $30,000,000.

Certainly the centerpiece of the report was the proposal for the construction of the storage reservoirs, the so called "dry" dams. Indeed, the report asserted that they would give "complete relief from floods to the entire Miami Valley." But the proposal immediately became involved in controversy. Dry dams did not contain water directly behind them in lakes or pools; rather, through the interrelationship of channels, levees and conduits they kept flood waters temporarily in a basin to release them downstream at a controlled rate.

The pools formed behind the dams would dissipate in a few days and during most of the year the land there would be useable for farming or recreation, but not for permanent habitation. Morgan knew that the notion of dams without water permanently behind them flew in the face of conventional understanding and he carefully marshalled his arguments in favor of the concept. He cited especially the construction in 1711 of the Pinay Dam in France, which had helped control floods in the Loire River Valley. The fertile silt settling behind it during floods accounted in part for an increase in crop yields of thiry to fifty percent. Morgan himself had built dry dams in Missouri, but not on the large scale that he now envisioned.

Supporting Morgan's view was a consulting board of engineers appointed by the flood prevention committee. Composed of three distinguished mid-western engineers—Daniel Mead of Madison, Wisconsin, Sherman Woodward of Iowa State University and John Alvord of Chicago—this board issued in January, 1914 a strong endorsement of the Morgan plan:

"The system as outlined . . . will give safety and security to life and to the property interests in the valley against great floods, and we would advise that the work be continued on the assumption that a reservoir system will constitute the dominant feature of the protection work which will be supplemented by such moderate channel improvements as may be found necessary in each locality."

To implement the plan, the committee required permissive state legislation. John A. McMahon, a lawyer active in Dayton civic affairs for more than fifty years, drafted the proposal. Almost from the outset, the engineering plan and the draft of the conservancy law, as it was called, met opposition.

The "flood fund" grows (left); noon-hour parade headed by community leaders marches to the courthouse (below).

As Morgan later recalled it, people in the areas north of Dayton, engaging a battery of lawyers, took the lead in expressing objections to the dams that would be built largely in their counties. They were skeptical about the efficacy of dry dams, they feared the dams were intended not to control floods but to generate power for private profit and they predicted that farmers would be forced to give up land and pay substantial costs for construction of the system. Recalling the Civil War, they portrayed Morgan as the leader of "Morgan's Raiders." Morgan found that he had to be cautious in advancing arguments for the dams. At one point, he declared that they would protect the valley from any amount of precipitation, except that brought by another great glacier; the editor of a newspaper in Miami County promptly published a headline "revealing" that Morgan had doubts about the proposed dams. By his own admission, Morgan had failed to "educate" the people to the north.

To that task, Edward A. Deeds, then a vice president of NCR, addressed himself. Clearly, he was also speaking for Patterson. He gave speeches and slide shows (Patterson's favorite method of lecturing employees) at schools, churches and town halls. He often spoke of a future safe from the fear of floods threatening life and property, one in which the Miami Valley would grow in prosperity. Joining his campaign were the newspaper editors of Dayton. Counting off the benefits that would come from the security afforded by the dams, one editor published a cartoon emblazoned with the words "Make Miami Valley Mighty."

"I AM THANKFUL"

OBSTRUCTING THE WAY

108

Eventually, despite or because of the shrillness of the opposition, the Ohio General Assembly passed a conservancy act early in 1914, the Vonderheide Act. Appropriately enough, Governor Cox, who signed the bill in February of 1914, was a native of Butler County and a resident of Montgomery County. Among its provisions was one stipulating, that on petition for creation of a conservancy district, the Common Pleas judges of the counties to be included in the district would constitute a Conservancy Court that would determine whether such a district should be organized. Another provision set forth a rather unusual method by which assessments for construction of conservancy dams would derive from benefits realized by residents of the valley (see Appendix A).

At this point, the proposed district truly became more than a project of Dayton. Citizens of ten counties along the Miami River and its tributaries (Montgomery, Shelby, Logan, Miami, Clark, Greene, Butler, Warren, Hamilton and Preble) petitioned the Court of Common Pleas in Montgomery County in February of 1914 for creation of a conservancy district.

Anticipating legal challenges to the organization of a district and seeking wider support for the plan of construction, the flood prevention committee decided to create a second and larger consulting board to review the flood control plans. All eight members of this board were prominent engineers. Two were former chiefs of engineers of the U. S. Army; five had had direct experience in flood control projects.

Meeting in March of 1914, they thoroughly reviewed the plan for the Miami Valley and soon gave their unanimous endorsement to it. They offered strong support for the concept of dry dams and, perhaps attuned to the fears of residents in the northern counties, condemned any use of the reservoirs for generating power. Their report concluded on a vigorous note of optimism:

"Works of the type suggested, properly designed, located and constructed, will not only provide satisfactory and economical protection from floods but they will be so massive and substantial as to fully justify confidence in their integrity and satisfy every reasonable question of stability."

Opposition, though, did not cease. Residents of Miami County sought a writ of prohibition against the hearing of the petition for organization of a conservancy district, arguing that the enabling act was unconstitutional. Lengthy litigation ensued before the Supreme Court of Ohio found the legislation to be valid. At about the same time, opponents of the law were attempting to persuade the General Assembly to repeal the Act or amend it to death, but that gambit failed, as did another constitutional challenge. Finally, in June of 1915, the Conservancy Court met and declared the Miami Conservancy District organized (Figure 4). Affirming its regional character, the Court named three directors to the board from three different counties: Deeds of Montgomery County, Henry Allen of Miami County and Gordon S. Rentschler of Butler County.

Thereafter the District moved rapidly to its work. Deeds donated funds for construction of a District headquarters at the corner of Monument and Jefferson streets in Dayton. It is still there, appropriately enough within a stone's throw of the Great Miami River.

By the fall of 1915, a Conservancy staff was in place: the Administration, Engineering, Appraisal and Legal departments. And early in 1916, in accordance with conservancy law, the Engineering department had prepared the "Official Plan" for construction.

The plan, derived in its outlines from the proposals of 1913, fell into two parts. It called for the creation of five retarding basins by the construction of earthen dams across the Great Miami, Mad and Stillwater Rivers and across Twin and Loramie Creeks (Figure 5). Morgan's engineers selected the sites only after a careful and exacting consideration of various factors. They looked at questions concerning the width and heighth of valleys, bedrock for siting concrete outlets, upstream storage capacity and alterations of existing land use and transportation routes. They examined more than twenty sites before settling on a final five.

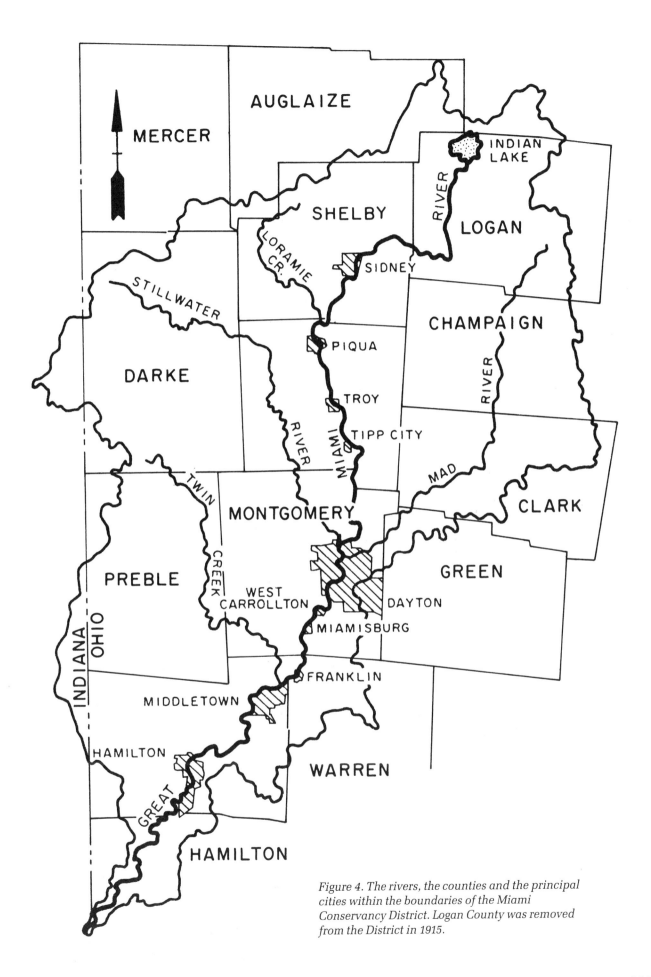

Figure 4. The rivers, the counties and the principal cities within the boundaries of the Miami Conservancy District. Logan County was removed from the District in 1915.

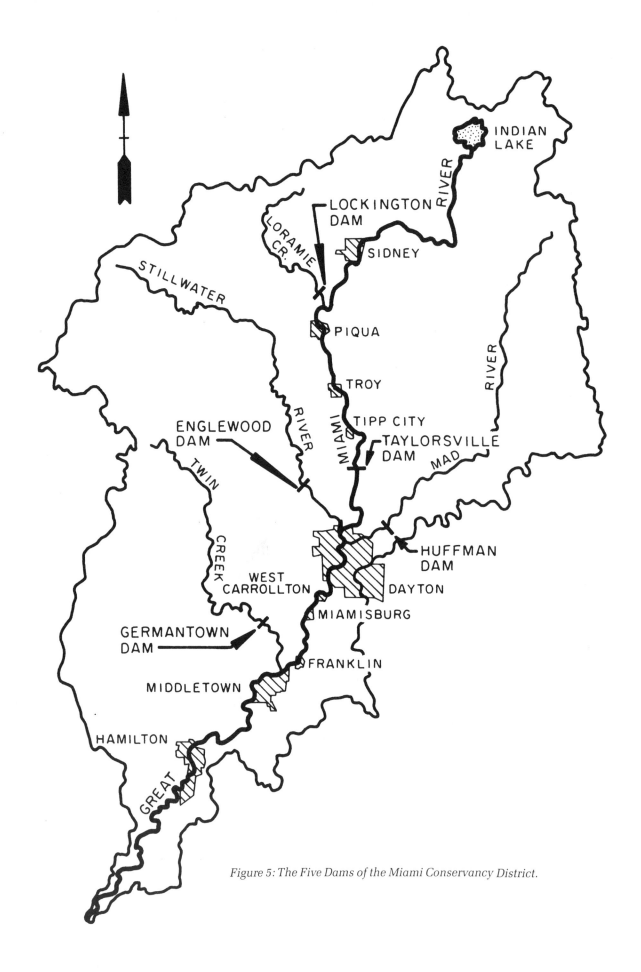

Figure 5: The Five Dams of the Miami Conservancy District.

The Morgan people also detailed in the plan their proposals for "local protection"—the building of levees and revetments along river banks, the widening and deepening of channels, the raising and lengthening of bridges to permit a greater flow of water around them and the clearing of obstructions from the channels.

Late in 1916, the Conservancy Court approved the plan. Nonetheless, litigation continued but at last waned when in 1917 and 1918 the Conservancy Court and Supreme Court of Ohio handed down decisions sustaining the plan. Now the District could go forth to turn promises in attics into reality.

Morgan rejoiced at the ending of litigation but saw it as only a beginning of an urgent mission. "The last days of 1917," he wrote, "marked an end and a beginning. The days and years of obstruction and delay were ended. As the time for construction arrived, the sustained vigorous pace which had been maintained was not relaxed, for the flood menace still hung over the Valley." Literally, the time had come to dig in.

The entire community was mobilized (left); the night they reached the $2,000,000 goal (below).

Building For The Ages

Early in his planning, Morgan had decided not to hire private contractors to carry out construction for the District, as was traditional when public entities took up capital projects. Instead, the District itself would take on all the construction and all the necessary support activities.

It would purchase building equipment, erect shops and warehouses, recruit the work force and build houses for them at the dam sites, lay railroad track, build barges and assemble a fleet of vehicles. That was the most practical and efficient way, he believed, to undertake the largest construction project in the nation up to that time.

As the District was preparing the Official Plan, it was taking up a gigantic task in appraising property for the assessments that were necessary to support the issuance of bonds for financing construction. Ordinarily, an appraisal of benefit derived from a determination of the direct increase in the market value of property resulting from an improvement, in this instance a flood control system.

But, the District benefits were based on the preservation or restoration of previously existing market values. Thus its appraisers sought to assess the market value of property before the flood, less physical destruction caused by the flood, and then to estimate the benefit stemming from protection. They also had to determine damages to property values on land the District had to acquire for construction purposes.

About one hundred field inspectors, supported by a large staff of engineers and clerical workers, appraised about 77,000 parcels of land owned by individuals, business concerns and governmental bodies. The initial compiliation of benefits in the District amounted to more than $100,000,000—a figure three times greater than the estimated $30,000,000 cost of construction. (See Appendix A.)

The benefits in five counties—Miami, Montgomery, Warren, Butler and Hamilton—were reduced to $77,000,000, with $38,000,000 for individuals and $39,000,000 for municipal and county governments. About 1900 property owners filed exceptions to the appraisals of benefits or damages; of these, about 500 were appealed to the Conservancy Court, and around 150 ultimately took their cases to a trial by jury.

By 1917, as the District prepared for a kind of battle against the elements, the nation was entering the Great War against Germany. Necessarily, the military effort tightened the market for men, money and materials. Nonetheless, the District moved vigorously and successfully.

Conduit construction at Lockington; two guyed derricks handled forms and concrete.

Gravel washing and concrete mixing plant at Englewood; upstream end of conduits are visible.

In its search for credit, the District had to compete with the national government, which was issuing a variety of securities and selling them in patriotic campaigns. With a bit of pulling and tugging, the District received clearance from the Secretary of the Treasury to market bonds. Early in 1918 an issue of more than $24,000,000 was sold, followed by an additional issue of $10,000,000 more. The bonds carried an interest rate of 5.5% and although they were not redeemable prior to the end of their 30-year term, both issues were snapped up quickly. It was, at the time, the largest special-assessment bond issue for flood control in the nation's history.

Even earlier, Morgan had initiated a thorough national search for engineering personnel. Between 1914 and 1917, his office received more than 3,000 applications. After the best prospects had been sorted out, Morgan conducted personal interviews. On one trip alone, he interviewed 50 men.

The engineers finally employed, about 50 men, had worked on projects in many countries: in Holland, Canada, Norway, Austria and China, among others. One had helped build a highway in the Andes Mountains; another had assisted in designing the Gatun Dam on the Panama Canal.

Appointed construction manager was Charles Locher, who had won his spurs for his work on the Chicago Drainage Canal, the Shoshone Dam, the Catskill Aqueduct and other major projects. He had a reputation for breaking beyond conventional building barriers, but not dangerously so. Locher's assistant was Charles Paul, reputedly a "master" of construction engineering.

Besides the engineers, other men played a significant role in the District's work. Certainly among them were William "Big Bill" McIntosh, chief mechanic of the Construction Plant; Fowler Smith, the purchasing agent who made key decisions

Building first submerged cross weir at Huffman Dam, at lower end of hydraulic jump pool; this is a good view of the supporting trestle work (above). Below, cableway drums, engine and boiler in use in Hamilton in 1920; front drum is hoist line, rear drum the endless line.

in the acquisition of equipment; and F. L. Cavis, chief accountant, who had myriad fiscal responsibilities to meet. Recruited largely in the Miami Valley, the mechanics in the machine shop and the construction workers on the dams and local improvements numbered above one thousand; no one of them was indispensable but collectively they were the life blood of the great enterprise.

Scouring the nation, the Morgan men led by Locher had acquired nearly all the requisite construction equipment by February of 1918. It was an impressive array of technology of the time: 18 drag lines, 29 locomotives, 200 dump cars, 80 trucks and automobiles, 15 miles of railroad track and 73 miles of high-voltage electric transmission lines.

The drag lines particularly proved an elusive and intractable quarry. Fowler Smith and McIntosh found a big Bucyrus machine in an open mine in northern Michigan and had to employ a gang of men to shovel snow six feet deep for a quarter mile in order to move it as the temperature fell to 35 degrees below zero. Morgan had three machines dug out of the snow in a drainage canal near Chicago and two very large ones dragged from a swamp in Mississippi. All these machines had to be taken apart and transported to Dayton where the District's machine shop overhauled and reassembled them.

Meanwhile, the District was making ready a construction plant and a central warehouse out of an industrial building and an adjacent structure in Dayton. The warehouse later supplied construction sites with tools, hardware, work gloves, rubber boots and other necessary items.

The builders of the Taylorsville outlet pause for a group portrait on August 11, 1920.

At the construction plant, the heavy-duty machine shop was the hub of the work. Supervised by McIntosh, the shop employed 50 mechanics engaged in every sort of heavy equipment repair. The repair work was critically important because the District could not readily purchase new equipment in the war-time economy. As Morgan remembered him, McIntosh had but one aim: to see that no broken or faulty equipment caused a delay in construction.

"If a telephone message was received telling of a serious break in a machine which needed his personal attention, he was off," wrote Morgan, "bouncing over the rough roads like an old-time doctor in a race with the stork."

The shop had excellent facilities for its tasks. Through it ran a railroad track permitting movement of heavy pieces of equipment within reach of an overhead 15-ton travelling crane. Mechanics there were busy operating lathes and other machine tools, and a compressed air distribution system enabled them to use pneumatic drills, riveters and hammers. Annually, the cost of repairs was about $300,000.

The shop's machinists took pride in their work, often boasting that reconditioned machines left the shop in better than new condition. They also designed improvements in machinery that made for greater efficiency and practicality. Their use of "white iron" (a more malleable cast iron) rather than steel for repairs and their techniques of thickening dredge shells at key points were typical examples of their innovative efforts. Out of the work in the shop, Paul later published a report on dragline design that Morgan viewed as the first

A view of the general shop yard in Dayton, November 1918.

adequate treatment of the subject and which became a classic study in the field.

Even before all the equipment and support facilities were completely ready, construction began in January of 1918 when excavation for a railroad siding took place at the site of what became Huffman Dam.

In the light of the massive project that was thus underway, some observers perhaps thought it strange that no ceremony attended the event. But Morgan had no inclination for silver spades and ribbon-cutting. The next five years saw a concerted effort—a great mixing of ideas, men, materials and money—in raising up five large earthen dams and in effecting improvements in levees and channels, the so-called local protections.

In the construction of the dams and the local projects, the District engineers employed innovative technology and unusual improvisations. Indeed, drawing on the experience and success gained in the project, some of the engineers authored a number of significant technical reports, articles and books.

The District's fleet of trucks at the general garage, August 1918 (above); the stenographic staff (below) and draftsmen (bottom) at work in District headquarters, February 1916.

121

The District's surveyors, some "dressed like cowboys," covered a lot of ground (above).

Building a culvert at Picayune Creek, three miles north of Taylorsville Dam, required construction of a dumping trestle (right).

Wooden model of the hydraulic jump, tested in Col. Deeds' swimming pool (below).

Certainly the introduction of the "hydraulic jump" at the dams was a remarkable innovation. This development stemmed directly from Morgan's decision to create retarding basins behind the earthen dams. Accumulated flood waters in the basins had to flow through discharge conduits in the dams; the conduits would not permit more water to be emitted than could be safely handled by the downstream channel. Several days might elapse before the pool behind the dam would be discharged.   But there was a key problem in this design. At the time of a flood, water would be forced out of the conduits at high pressure and great velocity. Unless the kinetic energy thus created was somehow dissipated, the force of the water might erode the river channel below the dam, eat its way back upstream and undermine the dam. At one of the dams, engineers estimated that a full basin would discharge more than 50,000 cubic feet of water per second and generate 150,000 horsepower. How could the dams harmlessly release this tremendous energy?

The solution was the hydraulic jump. Sherman Woodward, Ross Riegel and John Beebe, three of Morgan's engineers, developed the theory and practice of the jump, using the swimming pool at Deeds' Moraine Farm estate as their hydraulic laboratory. They designed the conduits of the dams to feed water down an inclined plane over a weir, or low dam, into a "stilling pool." Backwater from below tended to pile on top of the pool and created a standing wave, thus destroying the kinetic energy by internal friction. Anyone who has ridden

View of hydraulic jump pool from top of the wall at Lockington just before water was allowed in through entrance channel June 11, 1919.

a whitewater raft down the New River or through the Grand Canyon will recognize the effect of standing waves.

In the design of the hydraulic jump, the Miami Conservancy District made an important and original contribution to the field of hydraulic engineering. The jumps were the first of their kind ever built and Woodward, Riegel and Beebe authored technical reports on them that remain today as fundamental sources for their design.

The District also earned some repute for its use of hydraulic fill in the construction of the dams. Its application called for a fairly simple but interesting technology. The fill—sand, gravel and clay—came from huge "borrow" pits excavated in hillsides near the sites of the dams.

Power shovels usually dug in the pits for the raw materials. After water was mixed in to form a "slurry," dredge pipes pumped the fill to the dams. In some instances, "hydraulic monitors" excavated the borrow pits. The monitors shot powerful jets of water through nozzles into the hillsides and, reminiscent of scenes of the California gold rush, washed the earth into sluices and thus onto the dam sites.

In either case, the water gradually drained away and the dam rose in layers of impervious clay in the center, forming a waterproof core; the sand and gravel then formed the faces of the dams. The District did not make the first use ever of the hydraulic fill but it did make one of the largest such applications in history.

At the sites of local protection, the District engineers employed some interesting methods of construction as well, especially the use of flexible revetment. The engineers were

The hydraulic jump in action at Germantown during flood of April 15, 1922,
looking upstream (above); at left, similar action at Englewood on the same day.
Below, the downstream side of the Taylorsville Dam with a particularly good
view of the bridge, spillway and hydraulic jump, January 1922.

Building Englewood Dam in May 1919 (above), looking west along centerline showing cutoff trench in the foreground and hydraulic fill in distance.

At Huffman Dam, April 1920, a hydraulic fill monitor discharges 3800 gallons per minute at 140-ppi pressure (above); hydraulic fill at Englewood, February 1919, with 15-inch cast-iron dredge pumps, one electric and the other steam. Class 24 Bucyrus draglines in distance (right).

concerned about protecting levees and river beds against the speeded flow of water caused by the channel improvements.

They used relatively conventional technology in building concrete retaining walls to protect levees from erosion and in constructing revetments at the outside bends of curved channels. But in protecting the river beds at the foot of banks they decided to use flexible revetments rather than a solid slab of concrete. Cast by the Price Brothers Company and transported to sites of construction, the flexible revetments consisted of concrete blocks, each 12 inches by 24 inches by 5 inches; they were tied together and linked into a flexible mat by galvanized iron wire ropes. Unlike the solid slab, they would not readily crack and break up.

(Paranthetically, the blocks represented a dividend for the industrial life of Dayton. The Price Brothers Company, then located in Michigan, had received a contract from the city of

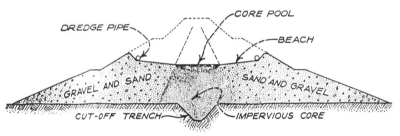

One of the best pictures of hydraulic fill operations, taken at Englewood, April 1919, shows giant pumps in action, rail cars dumping fill (above). Diagram at left shows how hydraulic fill worked.

Dayton to build the Island Park dam following the flood. Then its president, Harry Price, believing that the company could benefit from ties with the District's engineering staff, decided to relocate it in Dayton. Later it won a contract for manufacturing the revetment blocks, turning out ultimately 400,000 of them. The firm is still in Dayton and is known nationally as a leader in concrete technology.)

In support of its ultimate construction goals, the District took up several ventures revealing the practical creativity of its leadership. At Germantown, the nearest railroad line was three miles from the site of construction and separated from it by rough, hilly country. But the District somehow had to get a locomotive and dump cars there to move heavy loads efficiently in the building of the dam.

Flexible revetments were another important innovation. Pouring plant and curing yards (above right); men position each block and tie them together with cables near McKinley Park, Dayton, October 1920 (above). Below right, a combination of flexible and solid revetments along bank of the Miami River opposite Van Cleve Park.

Perhaps inspired by the techniques used by work crews in the building of the Union Pacific Railroad, the engineers laid a temporary track, moved a train forward on it, took up the rear track and relaid it at the front. In this "caterpillar" fashion a 40-ton locomotive and 12-cubic-yard dump cars traversed unpaved country roads and the streets of Germantown to the construction site. At completion of work on the dam, the train retraced its route the same way. Residents of Germantown, though interested in this display of ingenuous practicality, nevertheless complained about the damage done to their streets.   Besides running a railroad, the District created a miniature navy to support its work of enlarging the river channels through Dayton, building levees and removing sand bars. It built several scows and a small steamboat, the *Dorothy Jean*, evidently named for John H. Patterson's daughter. A stern wheel Ohio river model, 75 feet long with a 20 foot beam and drawing about two feet, the *Dorothy Jean* made her

maiden voyage on February 27, 1919 and remained in service until December of 1920. Daytonians long remembered this little steamboat as it navigated the Great Miami River through the city's downtown.

District engineers faced challenges in the relocation of railroad lines. Such relocation had to be completed before work could begin on dams because the old track would be blocked by construction. At Taylorsville, the engineers moved the main line of the Baltimore & Ohio railroad (the old CH&D) along the Great Miami River to higher ground for a distance of nearly ten miles.

Their greatest task was at Huffman Dam. There they had to relocate the mainlines of the Erie and the New York Central (the old Big Four) roads for fifteen miles and the Ohio Electric railway for ten miles. It was an enormous earth moving endeavor requiring the excavation of nearly 700,000 cubic yards of dirt and stone. The resultant cut, just below the present Wright Brothers Memorial, was 120 feet deep and 4800 feet long through solid rock.

The District effected a relocation of another sort in moving the entire village of Osborn. Because the village—its population numbered 200—lay on a flood plain that would be submerged after the construction of Huffman Dam, it had to be moved. Though the District "bought" the village, owners of homes could have their houses transported to a new site where the corporate existence of Osborn would continue.

A strip of land, 100 feet wide and two miles long, connected the village's old and new sites. The Osborn Removal Company began the relocation in 1921, moving houses at the speed of one mile in 90 minutes. Once the move was complete, the village legally eliminated the old site from its corporate boundaries and sustained its legal existence at the new site. About 30 years later Osborn merged with the village of Fairfield to form the present city of Fairborn.

In their general approach to engineering problems, District

Looking downstream just below Island Park dam, March 1920; flexible revetment warps but holds to protect bank.

engineers took their direction from two innovative policies,
one known as "dynamic design" and the other as "conclusive
engineering analysis." Both were bold new approaches in that
decade but became common practice later.

By dynamic design an engineer meant that he always
considered the design of a project to be fluid, subject to
modification as circumstances dictated. Engineers trained to
accept a design as fixed, static and unalterable could verge
towards nervous collapse when working in an environment
where design would change frequently and perhaps be settled
only days before actual work began. Such was the case even
among engineers working under Morgan for the TVA two
decades after the Miami Conservancy District's staff had
successfully employed the concept.

Pride of the District's navy was the
Dorothy Jean, *a sternwheel steamboat
built and launched on the banks of
the Miami River (upper); she waits as
a District-built scow is loaded just
above the Main Street bridge during
Miami River construction, April 1919
(below).*

Corollary to dynamic design was conclusive engineering analysis. It called for exploration of every possible solution to a problem whether promising or not. As Morgan saw it, engineers often accepted the first adequate solution, eschewing other lines of inquiry that might lead to better answers but appearing at first unfruitful.

Morgan cited his own understanding of dam design as an argument for conclusive analysis. Dry dams with retarding basins, he recalled, were not the first answer to the problems of flood control in the Miami Valley. He had assumed that reservoirs with controllable gates would be the best solution but had chosen dry dams after researching many alternative solutions.

The District could not help but bear the innovative imprint of Arthur Morgan as a social engineer. Though a practical, hard-headed engineer, he was a social visionary concerned about the improvement of individuals and the community. His service with the District gave him the opportunity to advance his concepts. He saw the District as an instrument that might transform the natural landscape and become a force of progressive social good for the community.

In the early planning for the District, Morgan displayed his philosophy of social improvement in calling for the creation of model villages for construction workers at the dam sites. "Human wreckage," he asserted had been a terrible part of the price paid by the "glorious American epic of pioneering and nation building." A conspicuous tableau of that wreckage, he

Named for John H. Patterson's daughter, the Dorothy Jean *was a familiar sight on Dayton waters for several years as she bustled about her scow-pushing chores. Above, at work at the confluence of the Mad and Miami Rivers, June 1919; employees of the District's Dayton Division on an inspection tour, December 19, 1920 (below).*

pointed out, were the migrant construction workers who drifted from job to job. Ill-housed in tar paper shacks, surrounded by drinking and gambling halls and brothels, and living in squalid conditions at large construction sites where "no decent man would take his family," they became the victims of an irresponsible society. He would have none of that at the Miami Conservancy District.

At each of the five dams he had a village or camp built for construction workers. The camps certainly did not imply the seamy side of company towns well-known at the time to many workers in the nation. The District installed sanitary sewers, water lines and electrical services at all the camps. Married workers and their families lived in one- and two-family houses and unmarried men lived in bunkhouses of various types.

Around all the dwelling places was open green space. A mess hall served nutritious meals for 35 cents. Each camp or village had its own school for children, and night schools offered free courses to adults.

"Community Associations" composed of the residents wrote constitutions and by-laws governing their communities. The associations arranged for the building of libraries, community halls, tennis courts and baseball fields. Morgan saw the camps shaping a happy labor force and a positive social environment. His espousal of them represented a bright departure from the

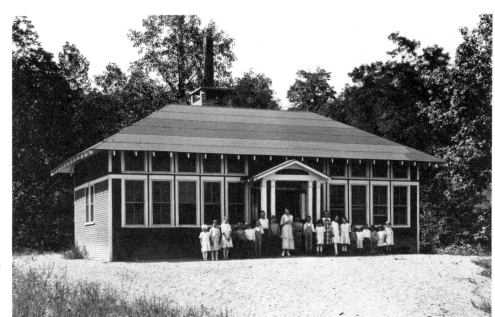

At each camp site, workers were housed in District-built villages such as this one at Germantown (bottom); typical cottage (below) later sold at auction when the work was done; schools and gardens also included.

Concreting operations at the outlet end Englewood Dam, March 1919 (above).
Topping off at Germantown Dam (below), November 1920, clearly show the hydraulic
fill idea in use.

Social Darwinism prevailing in many areas of industrial relations in the nation.

The District and Morgan also broke new ground in labor relations. At the time, 28 different unions in the area could claim jurisdiction on segments of construction. Seeking to avoid the conflicting jurisdictional claims and inter-union conflicts that had occurred in similar situations in the past, Morgan analyzed all of the labor codes of the unions affiliated with the Dayton Trades and Labor Council and incorporated them into the Miami Conservancy Labor Code.

Then in a series of meetings with union officials, he secured their agreement to the terms of the code. Labor leaders, knowing that typically construction projects had been unorganized and non-union, were eager to support the code.

The Board of Directors of the District adopted the code in 1918. Among its important provisions were the right of workers to organize into unions and bargain collectively, recognition of the eight-hour work day, time-and-one-half for overtime and the determination of wages solely by level of skills. Morgan believed that employment of a man should derive essentially from his character and workmanship.

Even after a short-lived wildcat strike called without notice, and the consequent advice of local industrialists that he drive organized labor from the project, Morgan insisted on the right of workers to organize unions. He argued that the proper course was one by which the District would earn the "loyalty of employees by fair play and goodwill."

For five years the District pursued its mammoth endeavor, overcoming in the process a variety of obstacles: petty but distractive litigation, a strike, a minor flood and the resignation of important personnel, including Morgan in 1921.

The engineers followed nearly identical methods of construction at all the dams. They had carefully chosen the

Improvised drydock north of Main Street as 40' x 80' scow is tilted so men can caulk seams.

Excavating rock to make way for the spillway at Taylorsville, April 1919.

sites so that the dams could be built at points where the valleys narrowed to a suitable width and where the underlying bedrock would support the dams and outlet works. They excavated into bedrock to install the outlet conduits and raised up massive concrete buttresses to support spillways and the upper portions of conduits.

Typically here were the only concrete sections of the dams; clay, gravel and sand formed the remainder of the structures. The engineers and construction workers poured concrete and piled up the earth day after day, and on April 17, 1923, again with little fanfare, the District could declare that it had reached a historic milestone: completion of the Official Plan.

No great monument was raised to celebrate and

commemorate the construction triumph. But each person who had participated in the labor might well have said of himself *Si monumentum requiris circumspice* (To see my monument just look around).

As he prepared to embark on the mighty work of constructing the dams and flood walls of the Miami Conservancy District, Morgan in 1917 characterized the effort thusly:

"All through the design our patron saint has been not the Greek architect who could design a beautiful structure, graceful and slender, but rather Pharaoh, who built his pyramids on so broad a base that no matter what mistakes of judgement might be made, or how faulty the work might be

Tractor and wagon haul fill for east wall of the Taylorsville spillway (above); an immense amount of excavation was needed for spillway (right).

done in the building, they would yet stand through the thousands of years.''

Morgan's analogy to the pyramids was apt in yet another way. The Great Pyramid of Cheops stands as tall as a 40-story building and has a volume of 3,500,000 cubic yards, a monumental structure in any time and by any reckoning. But before they were finished, the men of the Miami Conservancy Distrct had dug, carried, pushed, shovelled and rearranged a volume of earth equivalent to almost five such pyramids.

He and his fellow laborers might also have recited statistical data bearing testimony to the impressive dimensions of their work:

Two miles west of Germantown on Twin Creek, they built a dam of 865,000 cubic yards of earth. It is 100 feet high and has a crest of 1210 feet. During the flood of 1913 this dam, the engineers calculated, would have reduced the flow in Twin Creek from 66,000 cubic feet per second to 9340 cubic feet. The basin can store 73,000 acre feet of water over its 2950 acres of land.

On the Stillwater River ten miles northwest of Dayton, the men of the District constructed the largest of the five dams, Englewood Dam. The mass of earth composing it was 3,500,000 cubic yards, by itself the size of the Cheops pyramid. It rises more than 110 feet and has a crest of 4716 feet. At the flood stage of 1913 the dam would have cut the flow of

the Stillwater River from 85,400 cubic feet per second to 11,000 cubic feet. Encompassing 6350 acres of land, the basin can store 209,000 acre feet of water.

Just north of Lockington on Loramie Creek, the men of the District raised the Lockington Dam. Intended to reduce the flood crest at Troy and Piqua, it has a volume of 1,135,000 cubic yards of earth, stands 69 feet high and has a crest of 6400 feet. In 1913, it would have tamed the creek, reducing its flow from 33,000 to 8600 cubic feet per second. The basin behind it can contain 63,000 acre feet of water over 3600 acres of land.

About eight miles north of Dayton, District workers built the Taylorsville Dam across the main channel of the Great Miami River. They piled up 1,235,000 cubic yards of earth 67 feet high along a crest of 2980 feet. It would have cut the flooding of 1913 from 106,000 to 51,300 cubic feet per second. It has the greatest capacity of all the dams for outlet of water from the basin. Largest of all in the District, the basin is spread over 9650 acres. At a site six miles above the mouth of the Mad River and just below the flying

After the B & O railroad was relocated at Taylorsville, it was spanned by this reinforced concrete highway bridge (above); upstream view during construction of the weir at Taylorsville (below).

*Construction at Lockington, June 1919: water first entering the
hydraulic jump (above). Conduit construction (below) showing walls
of the entrance channel.*

field used by the Wright brothers in 1904 and 1905, the workers of the District could point to their labor on Huffman Dam. Here, they and their machines moved 1,655,000 cubic yards of earth into a dam standing 65 feet high along a crest of 3340 feet. Had it existed during the flood of 1913, it would have permitted the Mad River a flow of 32,600 cubic feet per second; in fact, the flow during the 1913 flood was about 78,000 cubic feet. With its 7300 acres, the basin can accommodate 124,000 acre feet of water. Because of the relocation of railroad track, Huffman proved to be one of the more difficult dams to build.

Unquestionably, the dams stood as dramatic symbols of the mission to protect the people from devastating floods. Yet, except for the prosaic labor that men did on the projects for local protection, the dams would have been slender reeds. Workers had to make river channels in communities in the valley capable of handling the maximum flow of water when the retarding basins were full and emitting their greatest discharges. Thus engineers and construction crews had to gather at the rivers for the widening and deepening of channels and the strengthening of levees.

Using huge lumbering dredges and draglines that gnawed away at the river banks like prehistoric monsters, they gradually widened and straightened channels. They took the spoils from river bottoms to use in the forming of revetments and levees. Old and obsolete factories and other buildings at the water's edge were removed, giving way to landscaped slopes and carefully engineered bends and banks. Occasionally, crews replaced bridges so that improved channels could carry a designated load of water at flood time.

They tamed and domesticated the old, meandering Great Miami within new banks up and down its course.

They took up projects of varying scale and significance. At Middletown, which derived substantial benefits from the reduction of the volume of flow in the channel, the channel was quite wide and construction crews had only to effect some

Hydraulic giant cuts into borrow pit bank at Lockington in the spring of 1921.

straightening and some improvements of the levees. Similarly at Miamisburg, where the channel also was wide, they merely built a levee along one portion of the river bank.

Their work at West Carrollton required only the construction of one levee to protect a low-lying area on the west side of the river. They also built levees at Franklin around low-lying areas and went on to widen and straighten the channel there.

They raised levees, enlarged channels and raised bridges at Piqua and Troy; at Troy they also cut a channel at a large bend in the river and thus shortened it. Concerned about the back-up of water behind the Taylorsville Dam, the engineers had the levees raised three feet higher at Tipp City than the crest of the spillway at the dam.

The District engineers had extensive, though not especially unusual, projects to work on in Dayton, where more than 18 miles of river bank needed protection. Workers built a series of levees and embankments, widened the channel and excavated it to a uniform depth, and installed revetments at curves from Island Park in north Dayton to the Broadway Street bridge at the southern edge of the city. The improved channel could thus carry the maximum discharge of water from the upstream basins and the unregulated flow entering the city between it and the dams.   At Hamilton, the engineers encountered an unusual set of problems. The drainage area above the city was half again larger than that of Dayton, but the channel here was narrower by more than 100 feet. To enlarge the channel even to a minimum width, the crews had to move 2,000,000 cubic yards of materials.

Huge dragline excavating near lower end of outlet conduits at Germantown in the fall of 1918 (at left); conduit is finished two years later (at right); building a bridge south of Germantown (below).

Special problem getting construction locomotive and cars to dam site at Germantown was solved by laying track on road in front of train, picking it up and re-using it after train crossed it (below). When the job was finished almost three years later procedure was repeated in opposite direction (right).

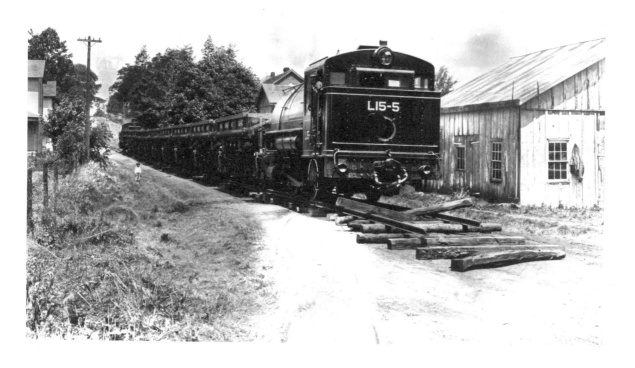

The depth from the top of the new levees to the bottom of the excavated channel—a fairly high 34 feet—resulted in a steep surface slope. Thus, during high water, the velocity of the flow would be swift. Consequently, the District had to provide extensive concrete protection along the east bank of the river and installed a substantial run of flexible revetment at the foot of the bank.

Additionally, because many buildings—including some large industrial structures—stood near the edge of the river, the District had to see to their removal. All seemed worth the labor, though. Engineers estimated that the flood flow of 350,000 cubic feet per second during the 1913 flood now would be reduced to a maximum of about 200,000 cubic feet.

The earthen dams and the local projects represented a massive calling together of men and materials. Altogether, the District people—the engineers, the mechanics, the clerks, the construction workers—moved more than 17,000,000 cubic yards of earth, almost enough to have built five of the great pyramids. They grubbed hundreds of acres of land, used over 4,000,000 pounds of steel, poured more than 250,000 cubic yards of concrete—the counting could go on and on—at a total cost of more than $32,000,000.

Wooden forms, such as these at Englewood Dam, November 1918, were built so concrete outlet conduits could be poured.

What counts, of course, is not a recitation of such data, staggering as it was for the time. The proof of the pudding, rather, was and is the protection that this immense labor gave and continues to give to the people. Through the years the dams and levees have proven of transcendent value to every man, woman and child in the Miami Valley.

Since their construction the dams have held back flood waters on at least 1067 occasions. Again and again, potentially disastrous floods have brought their waters against the walls of the great dams, and always the flood gates have dissipated them into harmless streams.

Even the devastating flood of 1937 that struck the Ohio Valley barely touched the communities that recalled the great flood of 1913. Though the Great Miami River in 1937 reached its highest stage since 1913, the water collected behind the District's dams occupied less than 15% of their storage capacity. Again, in 1982, when rainfall approaching the magnitude of 1913 inundated Ft. Wayne and many other communities, the areas guarded by the Miami Conservancy

District remained free of flooding. Through all the years no more than 60 percent of the capacity of the flood channels has ever been used.

The District has given a legacy to the world far beyond its impact on the Miami Valley. Noting its record in 1951, Morgan asserted that the District had fostered "new legislative implements, new concepts of labor policy, new engineering principles and new practices in management and construction."

The Taylorsville Dam spillway works lies under a mantle of snow and ice as 1920 draws to a close. Note the interesting little suspension bridge which carries the hydraulic fill pipe. Photo was taken on Dec. 28, 1920.

Morgan also pointed to the subsequent careers of men who had received their practical training at the District, which he described as an "engineering school for training masters in the field of river control, hydraulic engineering and general design and construction."

"Morgan's Men" went to all the corners of the world to ply their craft: to the Peruvian Andes, the Liberian jungles and Caribbean islands. They also took major assignments with a variety of employers in the United States: TVA, the Bureau of Reclamation, public power agencies, sanitary sewer systems and internal waterway authorities to name just a few.

Unquestionably, the dams and channels continue to stand today as a lasting tribute to a generation that aspired to build for the ages—that made and kept a promise.

Concrete mixer on railway car is loaded at screening plant, Englewood Dam, March 1919.

Looking downstream from the Englewood screening plant: outlet conduits under construction, March 1919 (below) and five months later completed conduits (above) carry water leaving river bed dry for dam construction.

Finishing up concrete outlet work at Englewood (above); view along centerline as dam nears completion in spring of 1921 (right).

Excavating for the outlet works and hydraulic jump pool at Huffman Dam; view is upstream.

Making the second 11 feet of the cut through Brassfield limestone formation at Huffman, June 1918 (above). Part of exposed face of south retaining wall and embankment side of north retaining wall in September 1919 (below); walls are 73 feet high.

An unusual view of the south end of Huffman Dam, August 1920, showing the railroad relocations (above).

The outlet works excavation at Huffman: tracks nearest the dragline used to haul away material, farthest track is temporary relocation of Big Four railroad (right). First cut, June 1918 (far right, upper).

One year later the cut is nearly complete and the retaining walls are being poured (above).

Although much of the excavating work was done by huge machines, men, mules and wagons did their share (above). Progress on the Huffman Hill cut (upper left), looking east, February 1919; view from the opposite direction showing temporary Big Four and Erie railroad tracks (left). The completed cut (below) looking west, October 1919.

First B & O train over relocated track July 7, 1920.

Local improvements required monumental earth moving and construction efforts, too. Short sections were built first to support First Baptist Church in Dayton (above) while the retaining wall was built. Unimproved conditions along Miami River (below) looking downstream from Dayton View bridge.

During work on South Robert Boulevard wall, gooseneck at top of derrick mast broke, falling boom struck and killed a workman (above). First five houses were razed and wall built so Miami River channel could be widened (below).

Job42-1454
6-17-19

Miami River improvements in Dayton: Dragline D-16 loads scow in mid-river (above) and works with the Dorothy Jean near shore (left). Both views are from the Steele High School tower; note historic Dayton Civil War monument (top) and Newcome Tavern (left).

The Herman Avenue bridge didn't prevent two draglines (top right) from working in tandem to clear the river channel, August 1918. The buckets were tied together by a cable which pulled one bucket while the other was drawn. Another dragline rolls onto a scow at a launching basin just below the bridge, February 1919 (middle right). High water in April 1920 wrecked this dragline above the Stewart Street bridge (bottom right).

Working on the South Robert Boulevard wall,
February 1920. Concrete mixing plant in center,
sewer manholes between track and wall (above). The
levee above Island Park, January 1919 (below):
McCook Field is on the right, Triangle Park across
the river on the left.

The levee in Piqua along East Water Street (above) and in Troy on Market Street (below) looked like this prior to the improvements.

Improvements in Troy involved the Miami & Erie canal and the Dye millrace (upper left);
another view of the millrace from Franklin Street (below). The District office in Troy
about to be moved from east to west Market Street by Charles E. Foreman, house mover
(left). The levee under construction in West Carrollton (above), July 1918.

Local improvements to streams
and banks were needed in other
communities north and south of
the main 1913 flood areas. In Tipp
City, the Miami & Erie canal would
need attention (above) as it also
would in Middletown: future levee
site at Titus Avenue and Hydraulic
Street (right); a retaining wall and
relocated sidewalk would be built
at Main and Hydraulic Streets
(upper right); the south bank of the
hydraulic canal would soon sport
a berm and a retaining wall (far
right).

Looking north along Dixie Highway at Franklin near Chautauqua, September 1918 (above) prior to levee construction and repaving. In Miamisburg (below) Bear Creek Road opposite the Sycamore Street bridge before the road was raised for the levee intersection.

Fourth Street in Miamisburg (above) shows condition of the street, February 1921, before it was raised to cross the levee. West Carrollton's Bridge Street (below), April 1919, before a levee was built on the right.

A pocket-size locomotive arrives in Franklin to help in construction of levees and road elevations. It is unloaded from a flat car to a truck trailer (below) and hauled to the work site (above).

The entire village of Osborn, on the flood plain behind Huffman Dam, was relocated near the village of Fairfield. Between 1922 and 1925, Osborn people moved some 400 buildings to the new site. The relocated railroad, interurban tracks and station during construction (above) and finished (below). Later the two villages merged to become the city of Fairborn.

Channel improvement in Hamilton was another immense task, the scope of which is demonstrated by these remarkable before and after pictures taken from the same place about three and one-half years apart. At upper right, a dragline dredging the river in September of 1919 keeps two trains busy hauling away sand and gravel. By April, 1923 the work is completed and the levee embankments are in place (far right). The size of the dragline bucket is illustrated (top), also a view of the river's east bank before work was started (above). The levee takes shape (lower right) in February, 1919.

Hamilton youngsters enjoy a dip in the river, August 1918, all but
oblivious of the dragline behind them building the south spoil bank's
first track environment (above). A year and a half later. the south spoil
bank nears completion as a train dumps its load of material (below).

At work on the Hamilton Drainage project in September, 1918; excavating for the Buckeye street sewer west of Front street (above) and another view looking north on Front street (above, left). The B & O stone arch in Hamilton takes shape with progress on conduit construction (below).

Vignette of a River:
Floods and Bridges

This book, a pictorial history of floods and flood protection in the Great Miami River valley, shows quite graphically that there is considerably more to a river than water running between or over its banks.

At times people and the vehicles of commerce must figure out how to get from one side of a river to the other. In the earliest days, a river was crossed at a ford. This typically was a place where a river had naturally widened so there was no deep channel with high velocity flow but rather a shallow channel over sand and gravel bars that permitted wading during most of the year.

Of course, fording rivers proved to be unsatisfactory. Often the shallow place was not convenient, other times it might be removed by the fierce currents of floods. In many times of the year fording was impossible because of prolonged high water or cold. So bridging a river was an enterprise to be undertaken early on by settlers in a new area.

Here is a rare pictorial history of all the bridges at a single location spanning the Great Miami River in Hamilton, Ohio. It uniquely records man's engineering achievements, the destruction wrought by floods, and reflects the expanding economy which we tend to take for granted. The irregular quality of some of these photographs is a reflection of very early or amateur work. Most of the photographs in this section are from the George C. Cummins Collection.

TBR

The first bridge across the Great Miami River in Hamilton was built in 1819. At that time the town on the east side of the river was named Hamilton; on the west side was the independent community of Rossville. Each had a central major thoroughfare, connected by an unreliable ford, until this covered bridge was erected in 1819. This importance of this particular photo cannot be over-emphasized. This view is copied from a daguerreotype taken on September 20, 1866, showing the bridge about to be washed away by a flood. Photography was in its infancy and dramatic shots of this nature are extremely rare. For the interest of local historians, the church steeple with rounded dome near the center of the photo is the Front Street Presbyterian Church; the steeple to the right is St. Mary's Catholic Church. The photo was taken from the Rossville side looking east; the communities merged in 1855.

The sign on the front of the three-lane bridge reads:

Keep to the Right

A Fine of $5.00 for riding or driving faster than a walk. A Fine of $20 for driving more than 20 head of Cattle or Horses or more than 100 Hogs over this BRIDGE at one time.

This suspension bridge, built in the manner of the Roebling suspension bridge in Cincinnati, replaced the lost covered bridge in 1867. This pioneering photograph, taken on May 7, 1868, looks to the northwest from the east bank. Note the normal level of the river.

Same bridge during the high water of January 6, 1890. This view, also from the east side, looks southwest. This bridge was razed in 1895 to make way for a larger capacity span.

The following year, 1896, saw construction of this steel truss bridge which could accommodate much more traffic and streetcar tracks as well. When it was built it was the largest single span bridge in the United States. This photo, taken about 1910, looks from west to east at the Soldiers, Sailors and Pioneers monument. The original Courthouse tower, prior to its disastrous 1912 fire, is also visible nearer the center.

This temporary piling bridge was erected to link the city's east and west sides in 1895 as the suspension bridge was taken down; the cable support piers have not yet been removed. This view is north, or upstream, from the west side.

Within two years of its construction, the steel truss bridge survived the devastating flood of 1898, pictured here. It was washed away on March 25, 1913 in that year's disastrous Great Flood (an illustration of its collapse is included elsewhere in the book). This view is from the west. Visible on the original, but not on this copy, is the Courthouse and its tower, shrouded by rain and mist.

The Great Flood of 1913 swept away all of Hamilton's four bridges, severing commerce and communication across the river. This pontoon bridge was erected immediately after the flood so people could walk from one side of town to the other, but it soon washed away.

A second, sturdier pontoon bridge immediately replaced the first one that same year, 1913. It was held in place by a stay cable strung from bank to bank.

A temporary trestle soon replaced the pontoon bridge, enabling the community to regain
a sense of normalcy as it accommodated vehicles and streetcars as well as pedestrians.
But it was threatened by this ice jam, February 17, 1914, but was saved when the ice was
dynamited and removed with a steam-powered shovel working from the bridge. The still
existing steel truss railroad bridge built in late 1913 can be seen in the background.

The present High-Main Street bridge is seen here on the day of its dedication, May 6, 1915. Work on major local
improvements by the Miami Conservancy District would continue for almost a decade. These improvements
included deepening the river channel, removing obstructions and construction of levees.

Sustaining The System

With construction of dams and levees completed in 1923 in accordance with the Official Plan, the District could not, of course, rest on its oars. It had to look to periodic repair of dams, levees and channel banks. Not until 1932, though, did any dams require more than nominal maintenance. That year, engineers repaired two concrete walls at Huffman Dam that were showing surface deterioration.

Ten years later, the District's chief engineer prepared a special report on the condition of dams and levees. He found them to be "generally in an excellent state of preservation." Seepage of water through construction joints and the subsequent freezing and thawing had caused spalling and defacement of concrete surfaces. The District made the requisite repairs and also waterproofed many walls to prevent additional seepage.

Two decades later, in 1962, District engineers undertook another comprehensive study of the physical structures of the flood control system and then effected a number of important repairs. The basic design of the great structures was as reliable as ever and the quality of the original construction was as good. The damage, which in no way threatened the integrity of the flood protection, was due to the inevitable and unavoidable effects of time, weather and gravity.

At each dam, engineers had to deal with the deterioration of conduit headwalls, of parapet walls and of construction joints. They removed unsound concrete, applied an epoxy bonding surface and introduced reinforced mesh to restore the concrete to its original line and grade.

The rivers of the Miami Valley have been channeled and controlled but have certainly not been bridled or repressed. They continue their inevitable geologic mission of transporting sand, gravel, mud and soil from the lands of the valley to the Ohio River. The relatively rapid currents in the narrow channels above the cities in the District carry the sand and gravel, especially during high water, to the wider channels in the cities. There the current slows and the water deposits its burden.

The removal of these deposits is a continuous maintenance responsibility for the District. To control the cost of removal, the District encouraged commercial gravel plants in Dayton and Hamilton to remove the sand and gravel deposits for use in making concrete. By 1950, such plants had removed about 2,000,000 cubic yards, saving the District an estimated expenditure of $750,000.

Huffman Dam handles a flood with ease.

Besides the continuous work of maintenance, the District managed a substantial amount of farm land. In opening years of its operations, the District had aquired above the dams more than 30,000 acres of farm land that would be subject to flooding. It intended to sell the acreage eventually, retaining the right to flood it as needed.

A Farm Department undertook the task of rearranging the tracts for effective disposition of building sites on the high land and for shaping efficient farming units from the rest. By 1944, all the tracts had been sold. The land sold was quite fertile, receiving as it did the rich silt that once had been carried away by flooded streams.

The District retained about 3000 acres above and below the dams, much of it heavily forested and punctuated by small lakes created by excavations for the dams. This acreage, Morgan argued, offered a grand opportunity for the development of public parks.

A terrible national calamity was ironically the means of translating Morgan's vision into the "emerald necklace" of park reserves which today encircles the city of Dayton. The Great Depression of the 1930s and the New Deal programs of relief and conservation offered the chance to return public recreational activities to the river's banks. The Civilian Conservation Corps and the Works Projects Administration built shelter houses, picnic tables and fireplaces. They graded roads and hiking trails and provided a variety of facilities in the woods and along the rivers. Today, the Dayton-Montgomery County Park District manages and maintains the reserves under a lease from the District.

In 1939 the District joined the Army Air Corps and the WPA in honoring the inventors of the airplane. Wright Brothers Hill, a high point of land overlooking Huffman Dam and the site of Wilbur and Orville Wright's first flying field, was developed as a memorial park. Handsomely landscaped and centered on a memorial pylon, the Hill remains a popular park for valley residents and tourists.

For about forty years, the District effectively sustained a complex of dams and levees representing a response to the floods that had struck communities in the Great Miami River Basin for more than a century, particularly the flood of 1913. Its mission thus defined by historical circumstances, it necessarily restricted itself to protection of certain areas in the Basin from flooding. Then beginning in the 1950s, owing to a convergence of various forces—changing residential patterns, environmental concerns and recreational interests—the District undertook a series of new ventures that widened and diversified its mission.

The Official Plan of 1916 had not called for the protection from flooding of all areas of the Miami Valley, especially uninhabited strips of land along the Great Miami and its tributaries. Though such strips were vulnerable to flooding, people moved into them in increasing numbers in the 1930s

The still-to-be-finished Taylorsville Dam at work during high water in the spring of 1922. This aerial photograph, from McCook Field's Technical Data Section, provides an extraordinary view of the hydraulic jump.

and 1940s and inevitably found themselves and their property endangered by streams overflowing their banks. Occasionally, too, industrial facilities lay in the path of flood waters.

Especially following high waters in 1952 and 1959, the District initiated new projects—"additions" to the existing cluster of dams and levees—to afford householders security against flooding. From 1956 to 1976, eight projects were completed at a cost of about $4,000,000. At the Miami Shores Addition near West Carrollton, at sites north and south of Middletown, at sites near Miamisburg and Dayton and in Piqua, District engineers raised levees, constructed bridges and deflective walls, built pumping stations, widened channels and removed gravel deposits.

The District was also widening its program of flood control in the 1950s and thereafter through the creation of subdistricts. By statutory authority it could form such districts for the management of water resources partially within and outside of its existing boundaries. As early as 1916 and 1922 it had created two subdistricts but had dissolved them by 1923. Not until the 1950s did it establish more subdistricts. Then, in slightly more than a quarter-century, it created five subdistricts, all intended to meet the needs of the people living largely in areas outside of the immediate reaches of the Great Miami River, usually near tributary creeks of the river.

Typical of these districts were the Southern Miami County Subdistrict and the Dicks Creek—Little Muddy Creek Subdistrict, established in 1953 and 1961 respectively. For the first, District engineers effected improvements in the Great Miami River channel to protect farmlands at the upper end of the Taylorsville Retarding Basin; for the other they improved the flow of Dicks and Little Muddy Creeks for the benefit of farmlands in Butler and Warren Counties.

The District also planned construction of levees, dry reservoirs and other facilities for the Clear Creek Watershed Subdistrict in Franklin and the Pleasant Run Watershed Subdistrict serving Fairfield. But it was yet awaiting in 1986 appropriate financing and additional planning before starting construction. The Conservancy Court dissolved in 1985 the Lilly Creek Watershed Subdistrict in eastern Montgomery County upon completion of channel improvements and the replacement of a bridge.

The Miami Conservancy District has long had a reputation as an innovator in dam design and flood protection. For more than thirty years it has also taken a lead in areas going well beyond its original mission of flood control. It embarked on an ambitious course in 1953 with its creation of the Water Conservation Subdistrict. The Subdistrict was formed to provide a water supply for domestic, industrial and public use and to regulate "the flow of streams and to conserve the waters thereof." Between 1953 and 1958, the Subdistrict staff and consultants reviewed a number of potential reservoir sites and evaluated ground water conditions in the watershed. This study culminated in a report which recommended the abandonment of plans for groundwater recharge and water quality control.

By the late 1960s the "times they were a'changing." The rising national interest in the environment, air and water pollution concerns and the growing influence of the environmental movement again brought the District into the forefront of water quality issues. As states and the Federal Government enacted legislation dealing with water pollution, the District shaped a comprehensive plan for water quality management in the Great Miami River basin.

Under the plan, the Subdistrict assumed two primary responsibilities: monitoring water quality and enhancement and protection of water and land resources in the Basin. Soon it was evaluating the possible overpumping of water and possible overdrafting of the aquifer in Butler County by the city of Cincinnati, which had purchased land in the county for a well system intended to provide the city with water for residential and industrial usage. Then in 1971 the Subdistrict

Germantown Dam blends neatly into its environment.

began a program for the collection of water quality data for the entire Basin, requiring the regular testing of water samples by a District laboratory.

As a means of meeting its second responsibility, the Subdistrict took up a project for control of wastewater around Franklin. At the request of public officials and paper companies there, it constructed a wastewater treatment plant costing $2,500,000. In 1973, the village of Germantown asked permission to discharge effluents into the Franklin plant. Seven years and nearly $3,000,000 later, an interceptor line for that purpose was completed. In 1983, it aided the village of Carlisle in developing a sewerage system connected to the Franklin facility.

The Subdistrict also became involved in wastewater programs in the northern part of the Basin. In 1973 it undertook modification of the treatment plant in Pleasant Hill near the Stillwater River in Miami County. Additionally, the

Lockington Dam looking north.

Subdistrict approved in 1978 construction of a treatment plant and interceptor sewer serving Vandalia, Tipp City and parts of Miami and Montgomery Counties. That construction began in 1983. Currently, the District foresees a lessened need to enter into such projects and expects to reduce its involvement in the wastewater facilities it constructed. As a recent report noted, the District has as its primary mission the maintenance of the "existing flood control system."

Through the 1960s and 1970s, millions of Americans, often urged on by presidents, physicians and physical educators, were taking up sports and physical fitness programs. Increasingly, they became enthusiasts for squash, racquet ball, handball—and for running, walking and bicycling. Perhaps as many as twenty million men and women began jogging and running in the 1970s and hundreds of thousands became avid bicyclists.

The Conservancy District, responding to local champions of physical fitness, especially the River Corridor Committee, made the Great Miami a host for walkways and bikeways. Following several years of discussion and planning, and using public and private funds, it built a bikeway and walkway in 1975 along the river in downtown Dayton. Later, in 1977, it extended the bikeway to the Warren County line; in 1982, it pushed the bikeway north to the Wegerzyn Garden Center. By 1982, the river bikeway ran over twenty-five miles north and south from Dayton. The District was also working with interested river corridor committee bodies in other communities along the river.

The District was moving in another recreational direction in the 1970s as it constructed or considered construction of low dams, or low head dams. Built across a river channel, such dams create a small basin for recreational use and enhance the esthetic appearance of the surrounding area. A low dam contributes to the scenic background of the urban vista by providing a wider, more attractive pool of water between the river banks. The dam has no effect on the viability of flood control nor does the small pool in any way increase the danger of high water. In 1975, the District constructed a low dam in the Great Miami River in Dayton along with a companion amphitheater on the river bank, a site often used for concerts and other outdoor entertainments. A decade later it was taking up proposals for low dams near West Carrollton and Hamilton.

Through the 1970s and 1980s, the District saw a great surge in recreational use of its four reserves in Montgomery County. Leased and operated by the Dayton-Montgomery County Park District, Conservancy-owned land around the dams became literally parks for the millions. Hikers, nature-lovers and picnickers coming into these areas numbered nearly 2,500,000 in 1986, about fifty percent higher than in 1975.

All the while the District was addressing itself to numerous maintenance projects. Every annual report from the 1950s on

More than 25 miles of bikeway have been built along the river's edge.

has recorded lists of repair programs on dams and levees, removal of gravel bars and rubble from streams, improvement of service roads at dams, and so on. Remaining abreast of new technology, the District began the installation of relief wells in the 1970s at nearly all the dams. The wells had as their purpose the reduction of pressure at the downstream toe of dams caused by pressure exerted on groundwater beneath a dam by water behind it. If not controlled, this secondary pressure could result in damage to the toe of the dam. As water gathers in a retarding basin, the relief wells flow and thus reduce the pressure to an acceptable level.

The District installed the relief wells owing, in part, to recommendations of its Board of Consulting Engineers. At the organization of the District following the 1913 flood and through the ensuing years, such a board has been meeting periodically to review the physical status of the dams and to make recommendations concerning structural adjustments. The board is generally composed of soil specialists and hydrologic engineers.

All great organizations go through periodic self-evaluations, points in their evolution where they look back to their founding mission and weigh their successes and failures in meeting those those goals. In the 1970s the District had embarked on numerous programs outside the purview of flood control. In the 1980s strategies changed. The District moved vigorously to again emphasize maintaining the existing flood control system as the primary mission of the agency. Their self-study urged the "staying out of the waste water treatment area; extracting the District from any obligation to operate and maintain existing waste water facilities and participating in but not dominating the area of water quality."

As the District entered into a new maturity in the 1980s, it was looking to the rational planning of its program of repair and replacement of physical facilities and to the mobilization of its financial resources to carry out that program. District engineers have been evaluating flood gates, revetments, crest walls, flood walls and so on to determine schedules for maintaining or "de-aging" them to their original functional levels. As one report has noted, as long as communities exist in the Basin, the District must view de-aging its facilities as its primary responsibility to the public.

At the same time, the District was winning a victory enabling it to meet its mission more expeditiously. It had lost direct control of the Great Miami River in 1979 when the United States Army Corps of Engineers claimed jurisdiction over the river under the national Rivers and Harbors Act of 1899. The District thus had to obtain permits from the Engineers Corps for making even the simplest repairs or construction along the river, a procedure that could and did lead to costly delays compromising public safety.

Englewood, the largest of the dams.

The Federal courts providing no relief, the District sought and finally received approval from Congress in 1986 of a bill exempting it from the Rivers and Harbors Act, the first such exemption ever granted.

It was appropriate. The local communities had given birth to the Miami Conservancy District; now theirs remains the right to nurture and sustain it.

Appendix A

Appraisal of Flood Protection Benefits and Damages in the Miami Valley

Author's Note: What follows is an article published in the Engineering News Record of November 16, 1922. It explains in detail the methods employed by the Miami Conservancy District in estimating benefits of flood control to individuals, municipalities and utility firms. The estimated benefit had to exceed the cost of construction by a wide margin to justify that construction; that is, the assessment for the issuance of bonds had to be far lower than cost of construction.

As the article notes, the Conservancy Court probably would not have approved construction if its costs had been only about equal to the value of the benefits received. As a matter of fact, original benefits were $78,000,000 while cost of construction was $33,000,000.

Historically, the District has used a 2:1 cost-benefit ratio to determine the need for issuance of bonds for construction of any project. Appraisers for the District determined benefits in this manner: if a property was valued, for example, at $10,000 on the open market and if it incurred maximum flooding of ten feet or more, damages under the District's formula amounted to 43 percent or $4,300. Using the 2:1 cost-benefit ratio, the property would have been assessed $2,150 to be spread over the life of the relevant bond issue. As of 1983, the District had collected $93,000,000 in assessment for flood control and had prevented flood damages estimated at $235,000,000. Interestingly, 1913 flood damages were $129,000,000; in today's dollars those damages would amount to $1,032,958,636.

The District must also determine maintenance rates for its ongoing maintenance program. That rate cannot exceed one percent of benefits for a property without approval of the Conservancy Court.

Reprinted from
Engineering News-Record
November 16, 1922

Appraisal of Flood Protection Benefits and Damages in the Miami Valley

Increase in Value from Protective Works Estimated on Basis of Flood-Time Depreciation—Equitable Distribution and "Flooding Factors"—Farm and Utility Benefits

CONSTRUCTION of the flood-control works of the Miami Conservancy District in Ohio was financed by means of special assessment bonds issued by the district. Under the Conservancy Act of Ohio the assessments authorizing the issue of these bonds constitute a lien against each property benefited, up to the amount of benefits assessed against the property. This lien is paramount to any other except that of the general taxes for state, county and city purposes. It was therefore of primary importance to make careful determinations with reference to each tract or property as to just how much it is benefited.

Benefit Appraisal—In the case of most land reclamation, drainage or improvement projects it is possible to make a reasonably accurate estimate as to the value of the land after its improvement, and the difference between this new value and the original value gives the amount of the benefit. In the case of the Miami flood-control project, however, the benefit accruing to properties in the cities of the valley could not be determined so simply. Real estate values were considerably disturbed by the 1913 flood, in fact some values were completely destroyed. Street pavements were torn up, and light, water and sewer systems damaged. Residences and other private property were destroyed or damaged and railways and telephone and telegraph companies suffered in the same manner. The protection of these properties against a recurrence of such damage and destruction constitutes a direct benefit, but it does not follow that the amount of damage sustained during any past flood is a direct criterion as to the amount such property may be benefited.

The flood had a tendency to depreciate property values, but after the immediate effects of the disaster had been overcome and plans initiated to secure protection, values were maintained at more nearly what they would be with protection actually accomplished. It was therefore difficult to estimate present values. Those obtaining immediately before the flood could not be universally used as a basis for the appraisal of benefits because they had in some cases been wholly or partially destroyed. This confusion in values tended to complicate the appraisal problem.

The conservancy law of Ohio fully recognizes the difficulties inherent in establishing benefits, and gives the three appraisers wide discretionary powers, while fully protecting the property owners and communities by a number of appeal provisions.

Two Basic Requirements—Two conditions in the relation of benefits to cost were of critical importance. There were (1) the total of benefits must warrant the expenditure, and (2) equitable distribution must be accomplished.

Unless the flood-protection project should benefit the property owners within the district in real, demonstrable manner by an amount exceeding the cost of the project, it should not be carried out. The bonds would have an adequate margin of security and would find a ready market only in case the total benefit should exceed the cost of the proposed works by a very large margin (a ratio of 3 to 1 between benefit and cost is a satisfactory ratio). The Conservancy Court would no doubt have killed the project in case the cost of the proposed works had been nearly equal to the resulting benefits, or in case of obvious lack of equity in the distribution of appraisals as between different pieces of property in the flood territory, or in case the benefit appraisals could not stand the test of common sense.

Magnitude of Work—Viewed as a whole the appraisal work was an undertaking of very great magnitude. About 77,000 separate pieces of property had to be dealt with, distributed along 110 miles of river valley. In about one-fifth of the cases, damages were concerned; that is, the property would be taken in whole or in part for the construction of the flood-protection works. The other parcels were affected by benefits only. Whether damage or benefit, the definite amount had to be determined separately for each parcel. As a preliminary step complete engineering and property data had to be compiled.

Surveys and the determination of flood outlines indicated what properties would be affected. Engineers then prepared real estate maps of the entire territory, including the cities, and determined the depth of flooding by the flood of 1913 on each individual piece of property and the extent of the physical damages to property resulting from the proposed construction work.

Since many of the data required by the appraisers were of an engineering character, it became necessary for the engineering staff to assume a large part of the work of compiling and classifying data. Obviously, a close co-operation between appraisers and engineers was indispensable to the successful carrying out of the appraisal program.

Benefit Equated to Depreciation—City property constituted by far the largest element of value in the district, and also that class of property on which the flood benefit was the most difficult to determine. It was not considered that the actual physical damage to any one piece of property in the 1913 flood had an identifiable relation to the benefit produced by flood protection. However, the depth of flooding during the 1913 flood was the basis of the curve of flooding factors, shown in Fig. 2.

"Flooding Factors"—The flooding factor was the device developed to insure a uniform determination of benefits on the town properties. Many considerations entered into the making of this curve. It is expressly emphasized by the engineers and appraisers that both the values and the variation represented in this curve are not generally applicable to other cases, or to property other than that considered in the Miami district, because of the large number of individual or locality influences concerned.

Generally speaking, the first-floor level of a house constituted the most important datum point with respect to flood height or submergence. When water reaches the first floor the habitability of a house at once is directly affected. Again, in actual flood-time experience the condition of a house generally became critical and the last remaining vestige of habitability was destroyed when water reached the second-floor level. This consideration in fact was largely determinative in fixing 10-ft. submergence as corresponding to full depreciating effect of a flood.

However, it could not logically be concluded that the flooding factors would be in direct proportion to depth of submergence between zero and 10 ft. With shallow flooding the injurious effects are small except in interfering with entrance to buildings, use of streets, etc. At about 3 ft. depth or more, water ordinarily enters the first story, the streets are no longer fordable, and a considerable proportion of the entire injury in property depreciation has occurred. From 3 ft. to 5 ft. swift velocities develop, ingress and egress to and from buildings becomes practically impossible, damage is done to furniture and buildings, and danger to life develops. From 5 ft. submergence upward the conditions described become aggravated, but the increments of depreciation are small, until substantially full depreciation is reached at 10 ft. flooding depth. The lower portion of the curve purposely was left somewhat indefinite in order to allow latitude for judgment. This is because property bordering on the edge of the water or having portions inundated to inconsiderable depths required a range of factors, varying from zero to as high as 20 per cent, depending upon the circumstances of the case.

These factors, described as applying to depreciation, apply conversely to the benefit resulting from protection.

Industrial Property—Related considerations governed the appraisals of industrial property. Special conditions, however, were always looked for and taken account of. For instance, if machinery was located in the basement it was exposed to injury the moment water entered the basement, and therefore the basement level was treated as first-floor level. Losses in machinery and similar shop equipment were in fact so prominent a feature of the flood damages observed in the past that a benefit appraisal fully equal in its percentages to that on residential or commercial property was considered appropriate, in spite of the fact that habitability and danger to life are not concerned, and that factory buildings are not often damaged or destroyed in floods.

Gain in Value by Flood-Protection—The next step was to determine that portion of the value of property due to complete elimination of the flood risk. It happens that there was a great decrease in values directly after the 1913 flood, due to the general realization of

the flood risk; and this decrease was in effect the reverse of the increase of value which it was desired to estimate. Stated differently, the benefit to be determined was held to be that portion of the original market value that would be restored through flood protection.

Often this restoration was anticipated, and the restoration of values took place on the mere assurance that flood protection would be provided. In fact, to a very large extent values never dropped, for before the first shock was over plans for preventing flood injury were in progress and the people were assured that pro-

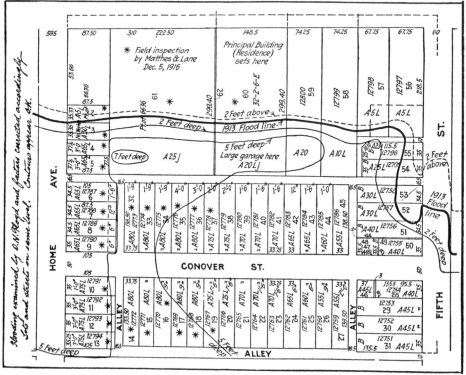

PARCEL PLAT USED IN FIELD CANVASS

Reproduction of a blueprint plat such as was used in determining flooding factors for city lots. It covers a section of Dayton. Contour lines indicate the water stage at the crest of the 1913 flood; in addition to the high-water line there are contours of the 2-ft., 5-ft., 7-ft. and 10-ft. depths, and a contour 2 ft. above water to indicate the rate of rise of the land not flooded. On each lot is written the flooding factor, preceded by a reference letter denoting the classification used and followed by the initial of the engineer who determined the factor. The asterisks indicate lots visited on field inspection. The numbers in feet and inches give depth of water on first floor of building at crest of 1913 flood. The serial numbers are those used in the tax duplicate.

tection was feasible and would be secured. Prior to 1913, property values in such valley cities as Dayton and Hamilton were practically unaffected by fears of flood, and it could fairly be assumed that the values prevailing prior to 1913 represented the values with full flood protection; on the other hand, the values at which property was held during the five or six months following the 1913 flood did not represent fairly the depreciated values on account of the flood risk, because values were maintained in the hope that protection would be secured.

Six or seven of the largest property holders in downtown Dayton and a number of representative real estate experts were consulted as to the permanent depreciation in property value that would result in the city from a failure to secure flood protection. They discussed the matter and arrived at a figure of 40 per cent of the value with protection, as the difference in value with and without protection, for the most seriously affected properties, and hence the benefit which would result from flood protection. The most seriously affected properties were the ones where the depth of flooding was 10 ft. or more, and where the flooding factor, discussed above, was 100 per cent. The same process was gone through in other cities with the help of corresponding groups of local men.

At a later stage of the work the figure of 40 per cent was reduced to 30 per cent as the basis of benefit, because calculations on this basis gave a sufficient total of benefits in the district for all purposes of financing, and there was no reason for encumbering the property beyond that point. However, the 40 per cent figure was then and still is considered a fair estimate of actual benefits.

In its simplest aspect the benefit appraisal consisted of first, appraising the market value of the property

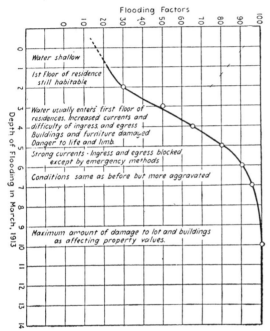

FIG. 2.   CURVE OF FLOODING FACTORS
Notes under the curve indicate the conditions which commonly existed at the various depths of flooding.

benefited; second, determining, for each parcel, the physical facts relating to its flooding conditions, especially during the March, 1913, flood; third, determining the completeness of protection afforded; and fourth, applying the flooding factor to the 40 per cent (later 30 per cent) of the appraised market value. Since the proposed flood-control works provided complete protection for city property in most cases, the third factor was 100 per cent except as to a few situations.

Benefits to Communities—It was held that the elimination of the flood risk would benefit cities and other communities as municipal units, as well as the individual pieces of property. Consequently benefit appraisals were required on cities, counties, etc., as units.

Taking the case of a city: The flood-protection works give protection to all property owned by the municipality as such, and to all the property constituting the wealth and business strength of the community. When a flood paralyzes industry and all principal forms of community and business life, as it did in the Miami valley cities in 1913, it affects every human being living in the community and affects the value of every piece of property within its boundaries. Thus the flood-protection project would guard the assets of the city and assure the future existence, growth and prosperity of

the community. That a destructive flood has far-spreading effects falling on the community as a whole may be seen from the fact, for example, that there existed for years afterwards numerous cases of pauperism, sickness, and insanity resulting from the 1913 flood; and such ill effects obviously fall as a burden on the community, and their elimination (for the future) constitutes a direct benefit to the community. Likewise the difficulty in a flood-menaced city of securing credit needed by business enterprises to properly carry on their business constitutes a definite deterrent to the normal growth and development of the city.

Upon considering the direct benefits to municipal property, and also the extensive but rather intangible effects of flood protection upon the city as a whole, it was concluded, after conferences with numerous officials, that the city as a unit would be benefited by an amount equal to the total benefits to its citizens individually. This conclusion applied to the larger valley cities except Piqua. For the latter a credit was allowed against the appraisal because of the fact that the city had already done certain work on its own account, and in consequence the city's net benefit was taken as half the sum of the individual benefits.

In determining the benefits to counties, the community benefit is not related in such clearly recognizable manner to the benefits accruing to individual property holders. Much county property was submerged and temporarily put out of use or damaged in the 1913 flood (and to lesser extent in the more frequent smaller floods). The values with and without protection of this property were estimated, and the difference taken as the measure of benefits. Loss of tax value resulting from the depreciation that took place after the 1913 flood was also carried into the benefit column, since similar loss of tax value would not occur under full protection. In all instances local business men were drawn upon for counsel as to the fairness of the values fixed on counties.

Property Outside of Cities—Benefit appraisals on individual parcels of country property were of necessity dealt with in a way quite different from that applied to city property. In the case of agricultural land, not used for residence, the injurious effects of flooding and consequently the benefit conferred by flood prevention probably would not be as great as on city property, and in some cases perhaps would be absent or negative. On the other hand, land which was ruined by either erosion or gravel deposition in the 1913 flood could not properly be considered to be benefited in high measure by future flood protection, as but little value remained to be protected. Creek bottom pasture land also had to be given a very low benefit estimate, as the actual gain here through elimination of future flood rises from the river would be almost negligible. Where buildings were involved, however, it was possible to base comparative benefit estimates on factors involving depth of submergence, somewhat as in the case of city property.

In the main the estimates for country property were in the largest measure based on conference of the appraisers with local experts such as retired farmers, after detailed personal inspection of the site and study of the flood conditions as revealed by the engineering plats. Agriculture benefits in the aggregate constituted less than 5 per cent of the whole.

Benefits to Utilities—Benefits to railroads were taken to involve the same quality and quantity factors as those influencing the benefits to private property. Appraisals were based on physical value, being guided to some extent by valuation figures of the Interstate Commerce Commission, plus land value. The latter was appraised on an area basis at figures equal to that of the adjoining lands. This work throughout required the co-operation of both engineering and appraisal departments. Here also the amount of benefits appraised was as nearly as could be determined the difference in value with and without protection.

Street-railway benefits also were appraised on a basis of physical value including the land value; the latter, being only a right-of-way, was taken as 25 per cent of the ownership value of adjoining land (per square foot) and was estimated for a width equal to the track width plus 18 in. on each side. To the physical valuation thus determined, flooding factors were applied similar to those used for city property.

Power houses in the flood territory were treated like other buildings, using the same flooding factors and basing on 10 ft. depth as full submergence. Those located outside the flood territory, on the other hand, were appraised no direct benefits, though they contributed indirectly to the project the tax rate increase caused by the benefit assessments against the city and county as units.

In valuing wire-line property in the flooded area, values taken from the companies' inventories were generally used as bases. Full benefit, corresponding to the 40 per cent tentative depreciation effect of the 1913 flood on individual properties, was taken as $12\frac{1}{2}$ per cent of the value.

This figure was later reduced 25 per cent to accord with the reduction from 40 per cent to 30 per cent previously mentioned, and the resulting figure was applied to the total value of the wire lines located in submerged territory. Similar methods were used in determining the benefits to other public utilities.

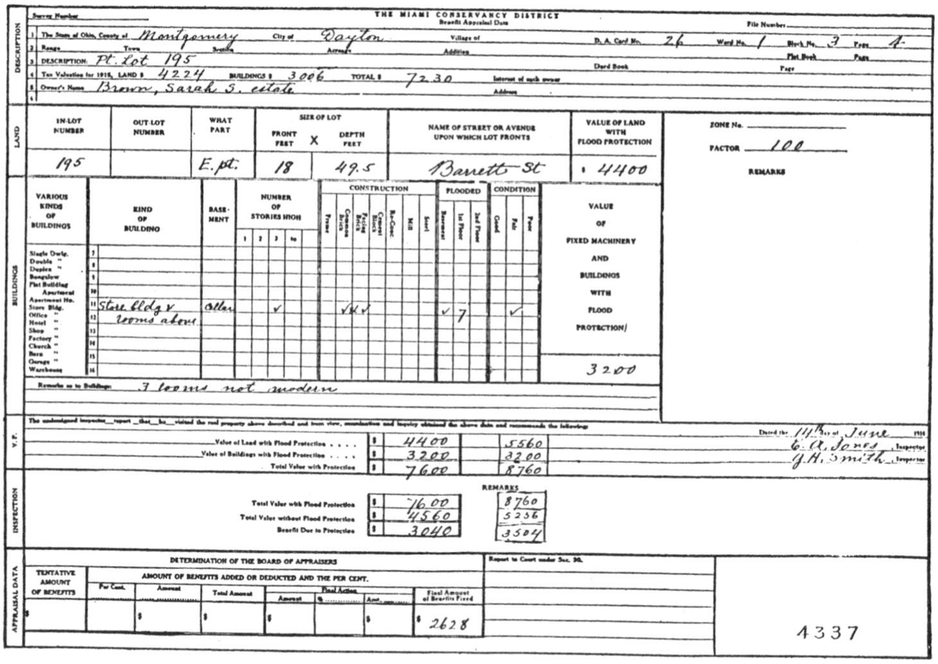

It is important to note that throughout the benefit appraisal of both public service utilities and large manufacturing establishments, the appraisers and their agents consulted with the officials of the various companies, and obtained data from them which enabled benefit figures to be arrived at which at once were fair and satisfactory to the companies. By thus enlisting the co-operation of the companies much subsequent disagreement was avoided, as evidenced by the fact that practically no exceptions were filed by public service companies or manufacturers. With about 100 public service corporations affected by benefits or damages, amicable settlements were reached in all but three cases.

Large Benefit Total Found—When the benefits were compiled and totaled, it was found that the entire benefit in the district amounted to something over $100,000,000. Inasmuch as only about $25,000,000 to

$30,000,000 was estimated to be spent on construction of the flood-protection works the ratio between appraised benefits and required assessments of benefits was considered to be unnecessarily large. Three times the amount of bonds to be sold for the construction of the works was believed to represent an ample benefit appraisal. Accordingly the initially determined benefit of 40 per cent for fully submerged property was reduced to 30 per cent, and all the appraisals correspondingly modified.

Of the nine counties included within the district, five (Miami, Montgomery, Warren, Butler and Hamilton) contained property that was benefited. The total benefits finally assessed in these five counties were: Individual benefits, $38,000,000; cities, $33,000,000; counties, $6,000,000; total, $77,000,000.

Damage Appraisals—The most extensive work in dealing with damages was that concerned with the lands in the retarding basins, which would be subject to overflow during flood periods, on account of the large areas involved and the novelty of the questions presented. Such lands as were actually to be occupied by the dams or used for borrow pits or otherwise necessary construction purposes naturally were bought outright and

FIG. 3.   BENEFIT-APPRAISAL RECORD CARD

remain in the possession of the conservancy district. Outside of this range, however, the basin lands are not permanently withdrawn from the agricultural service of the community, since only those in the very bottom of the valley will be frequently flooded, and those near spillway level will be wetted only in the conjectural, improbable rainfall-and-flood contingencies on which the whole project is based as an ultimate possibility. The upper lands of the basins, therefore, might be considered as being not at all affected by the exposure. However, the farmers, knowing but little about the engineering details of the project, necessarily took a different view, and their estimates of the damage to which they would be subjected differed materially from that of the board of appraisers.

Much Basin Land Bought—When this situation was fully realized, the district decided to buy in fee simple most of the basin lands. A smaller proportion of the total, chiefly the lands lying far up towards spillway level, was dealt with by purchasing an easement to put water on the land at irregular intervals, this easement including the right on the part of the district to require the removal of buildings from below a certain level, to prohibit all future building below a specified level, and in general to control the occupancy and use of the land so far as flood questions would bear on the matter.

The district determined a fair easement price on these lands after a field inspection, in which frequency and depth of flooding of the various tracts, the value and condition of the land, and other items were taken into consideration. This price, determined by the appraisers, was used as a guide in determining whether or not it would be necessary to buy the basin lands in fee simple.

FIG. 4. PURCHASE AND EASEMENT APPRAISAL DATA

Special procedure was adopted in a few individual instances, namely, an agreement was made with the owners of the land to pay damages due to flooding caused by the works of the district when damage occurs.

Land Resold—The lands in the basins purchased by the district have recently been put on sale, full information being supplied to intending purchasers as to the susceptibility to flooding and the probable effects of flood ponding upon the agricultural value of the lands. The net result to date is that an average sale price of about 85 per cent of the price at which the land was purchased has been realized, and in individual instances land has even been sold at higher figures than those paid by the district. Thus, it may be stated that the practical outcome of the methods used is to make the cost of the flood easement in the lower part of the basins about 15 per cent of the full value of the land. These figures are derived from sales representing about 20 per cent of the total area which the district expects to dispose of. As the sales continue these figures may have to be modified.

In proceedings under the conservancy law no separate condemnation of different parcels is required.

Accordingly, all the damage and benefit appraisals were submitted to the court in itemized form in a single appraisal roll, objections by property owners were heard by the court, and a decision was reached both as to the entire roll and as to individual parcels. The final court order contained both an easement price and a purchase price for each particular piece of damaged land, and the directors of the district were free to take over the easement or take over the property, at the figures entered in the order.

Results of the Appraisal—About 1,900 exceptions were taken by property owners to the appraisals of benefits and damages made by the district on about 77,000 parcels. Of the cases in which exception was taken to the district appraisals, not more than 500 were appealed to the Conservancy Court.

Expressing this in percentage figures it might be said that the district appraisal, carried out by the methods outlined in the preceding, proved something over 99 per cent efficient when measured by the attitude taken by the property owners affected, and substantially 100 per cent efficient when measured by the action of the court. In only a dozen or two cases were the exceptions and appeals made by the property owners effective in leading the court to modify the figures of the district.

Large Force Engaged in Work—As the whole appraisal undertaking dealt with some 77,000 parcels of land, a large organization had to be built up to deal with it. In control of the entire work there was a board of three appraisers appointed by the Conservancy Court, and consisting of J. Edward Sauer, Charles W. Kiser, and Samuel M. Goodman, three business men who were thoroughly acquainted with real estate values in the Miami valley. Great credit is due these men for the faithful and absolutely impartial manner in which they carried out the gigantic task assigned them. It required their close personal attention for a period of over a year, during which they had to sacrifice many of their private and other interests.

They were assisted by a large engineering and clerical force supplied by the district, a force of about 100 field inspectors alone being required. In the cities these inspectors were equipped with copies of the county auditor's plats, and in the country districts with plat maps supplied by the engineering department, upon which the flood outlines had been traced. The appraisers' inspectors were concerned primarily with determining actual values, which they entered on inspection sheets (see Figs. 3 and 4 for specimens), to be reviewed later by the board of appraisers themselves.

The appraisal board in person viewed every site and every parcel of property concerned, verifying and correcting the appraisals of the various field inspectors.

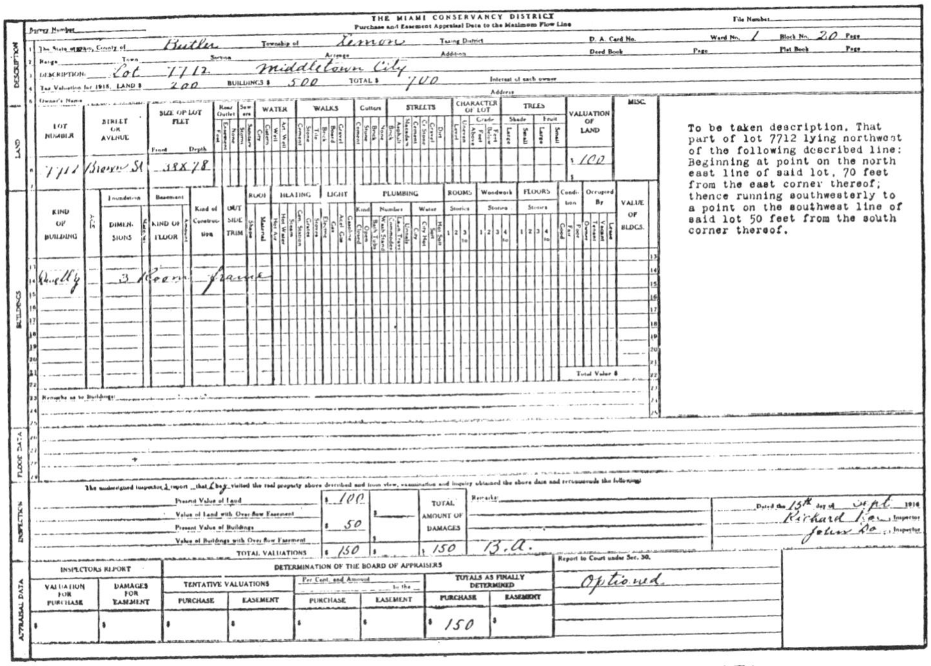

Appendix B

Conservancy Court Judges, Miami Conservancy District

Below are the names of the judges who have sat on the Conservancy Court since the enactment of legislation (Ohio Revised Code 6101.07) in 1914 authorizing the creation of the Miami Conservancy District. A Common Pleas Court judge for each county composing the District serves on the Court. In a county with more than one judge, the judges collectively decide who will represent the county on the Court.

Butler County

1914 Clarennce W. Murphy
1929 E. J. Kautz
1937 M. O. Burns
1939 Peter P. Boli
1961 Fred B. Cramer
1979 David Black
1987 William Stitsinger

Clark County

1914 F. M. Hagan
1915 Frank W. Geiger
1929 Golden C. Davis
1959 Ben J. Goldman
1975 Stanley Husted
1977 John W. Henderson

Greene County

1914 Charles H. Kyle
1921 R. L. Gowdy
1938 George H. Smith
1939 Frank L. Johnson
1941 George H. Smith
1943 Frank L. Johnson
1956 Dan M. Aultman
1978 Herman J. Weber
1982 Edward R. Kimmel

Hamilton County

1914 Otway J. Cosgrave
1921 Frederick L. Hoffman
1947 Dennis J. Ryan
1955 Charles S. Bell
1962 Louis J. Schneider
1971 William R. Matthews
1981 William J. Morrissey

Logan County
(removed from
District in 1915)

1914 John M. Broderick
1915 John C. Hover

Miami County

1914 Walter D. Jones
1938 Paul T. Klapp
1950 David S. Porter
1967 James H. DeWeese
1973 John H. Kistler
1981 James J. Hooper

Montgomery County

1914 Carroll C. Sprigg
1917 E. T. Snediker
1937 Lester L. Cecil
1953 Robert U. Martin
1971 Carl D. Kessler

Preble County

1914 A. C. Risinger
1938 Hugh R. Gilmore
1945 Don R. Thomas
1947 John M. Kiracofe
1973 Donald L. Ziegel
1978 John E. Ernst
1983 John V. Dye

Shelby County

1914 Hugh T. Mathers
1917 J. D. Barnes
1938 D. Finley Mills
1947 Huber A. Berry
1971 Frank M. Marshall
1978 Lieudell E. Bauer
1981 Carroll V. Lewis

Warren County

1914 Willard J. Wright
1929 Charles B. Dechant
1943 Alton F. Brown
1952 Frank C. Anderson
1956 Robert G. Ray
1957 Warren C. Young
1971 William W. Young
1987 T. Daniel Fedders

Appendix C

Board of Directors, Miami Conservancy District

Listed below are persons who have served on the Board of Directors of the Miami Conservancy District since its organization in 1915. Three comprise the Board. Appointed by the Conservancy Court, they serve five-year terms. They serve without pay. The Court may renew a term of office.

Edward A. Deeds	1915-1954
Henry M. Allen	1915-1926
Gordon S. Rentschler	1915-1932
Herbert L. Johnson	1926-1938
George A. Rentschler	1932-1950
Walter H. Coles	1938-1953
Stanley C. Allyn	1954-1967
Walter A. Rentschler	1950-1975
Edward A. Hobart	1953-1981
Robert S. Oelman	1967-1979
Roger Thyer	1971-1975
Lloyd Goggin	1975-1982
William H. Hobart, Jr.	1975-
B. Lyle Shafer	1979-1987
Thomas B. Rentschler	1982-
Gayle B. Price	1987-

Appendix D

From 1915 to 1970 two individuals generally managed the daily operations of the Miami Conservancy District, the Secretary-Treasurer and the Chief Engineer. Because the District was facing increasing responsibilities requiring a more unified direction, the Board of Directors decided in 1970 to vest primary supervision of the District in the hands of a General Manager-Secretary and then in 1985 joined that position to that of the Chief Engineer. The title is now Chief Engineer and General Manager. Appointed by the Board, the Chief Engineer and General Manager serves at its pleasure.

Chief Engineers, Miami Conservancy District

Arthur E. Morgan	1915-1921
Charles H. Paul	1921-1924
Curt H. Eiffert	1924-1949
Barton M. Jones	1950-1956
Max L. Mitchell	1956-1970
William T. Eiffert	1970-1972
Walter J. Linder	1972-1976
Donald T. Williams	1976-1981
James L. Rozelle	1981-

General Managers, Miami Conservancy District

L. Bennett Coy	1970-1985
James Rozelle	1985-

Appendix E

Board of Consultants, Miami Conservancy District

Even before the establishment of the Miami Conservancy District in 1915, the Flood Prevention Committee, at the suggestion of Arthur Morgan, engaged a board of consulting hydraulic engineers to evaluate proposed flood control measures. Since then, usually at five-year intervals, the Board of Consulting Engineers has met to review and assess the level of protection afforded by the Conservancy dams.

Reviewing the condition of the dams in the light of data collected by various monitoring devices, the consultants serve to help the District to weigh and analyze measures which might be needed to maintain or improve the flood protection. The consulting engineers, usually highly regarded hydrologic specialists, have always represented a great body of knowledge and experience. Altogether, they have worked on projects in eighty different countries and the current consulting board embodies more than three-hundred years of professional experience.

1913: Arthur Morgan, Daniel W. Mead, Sherman M. Woodward and John W. Alvord

1919: James H. Fuertes, Col. J. A. Ockerson, Brig. Gen. William H. Bixby, T. W. Jaycox, Daniel W. Mead, John W. Alvord and Arthur E. Morgan.

1929: Daniel W. Mead, Charles H. Locher, Sherman M. Woodward and Arthur E. Morgan.

1934: Daniel W. Mead, Sherman M. Woodward, Charles H. Locher and Carl A. Bock.

1939: Charles H. Locher, Joseph H. Kimball and Sherman M. Woodward.

1944: Daniel W. Mead, Sherman M. Woodward, Arthur E. Morgan, J. H. Kimball, C. C. Chambers, A. L. Pauls, Charles H. Locher and E. J. B. Schubring, attorney.

1956: Arthur E. Morgan, chair; Carl A. Bock, A. L. Pauls, T. C. Shuler, Francis S. Friel, C. P. Vetter, C. V. Youngquest and C. C. Chambers, secretary.

1962: Arthur E. Morgan, chair; J. Barry Cooke, Wilbur A. Dexheimer, Francis S. Friel, T. C. Shuler, Francis B. Slichter, Abel Wolman and C. V. Youngquest.

1966: Robert K. Dodson, Raymond A. Hill and Abel Wolman, chair.

1967: Edward J. Cleary, Raymond A. Hill and Abel Wolman, chair.

1971: E. T. Hellebrandt, R. A. Hill, G. J. Remus and Abel Wolman, chair.

1973: Robert K. Dodson, J. Barry Cooke, Richard D. Harza, Walter G. Schulz and Abel Wolman, chair.

1977: J. Barry Cooke, C. J. Cortright, Wendell E. Johnson, Ralph B. Peck and Abel Wolman, chair.

1979: Abel Wolman, Otto Anderson Davis, Harold G. Edwards, Myron Fiering, Thomas Maddock, Jr. and Richard C. Pickett.

1982: J. Barry Cooke, C. J. Cortright, Ralph B. Peck and Abel Wolman.

1987: Abel Wolman, chair emeritus; Ralph B. Peck, technical chair; J. Barry Cooke, Robert E. Philleo and Richard E. Burnett.

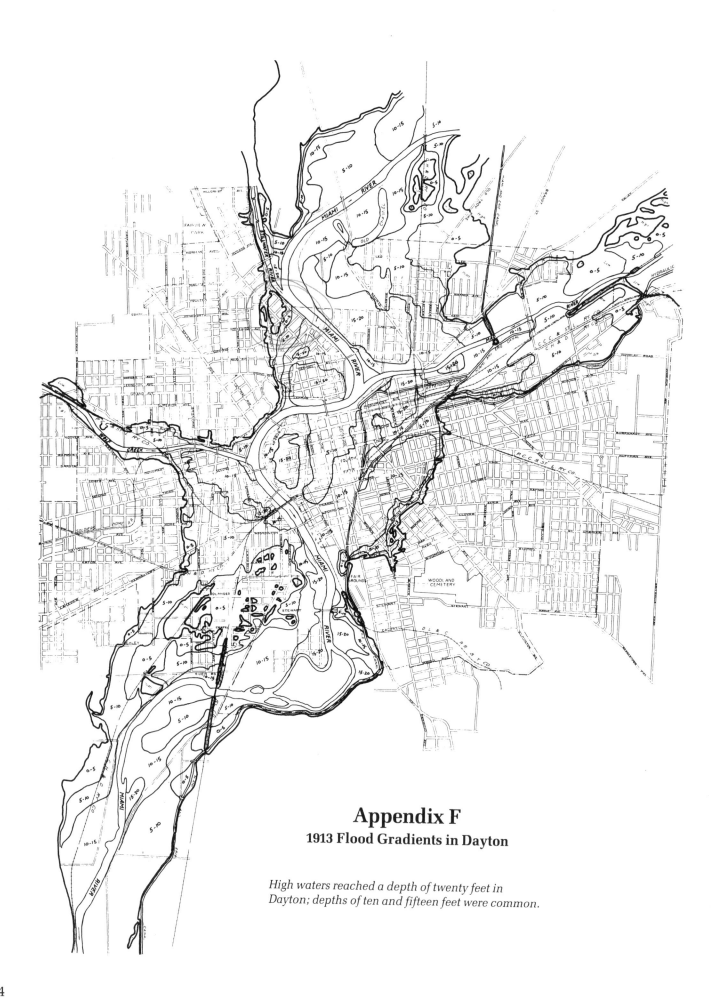

Appendix F
1913 Flood Gradients in Dayton

*High waters reached a depth of twenty feet in
Dayton; depths of ten and fifteen feet were common.*

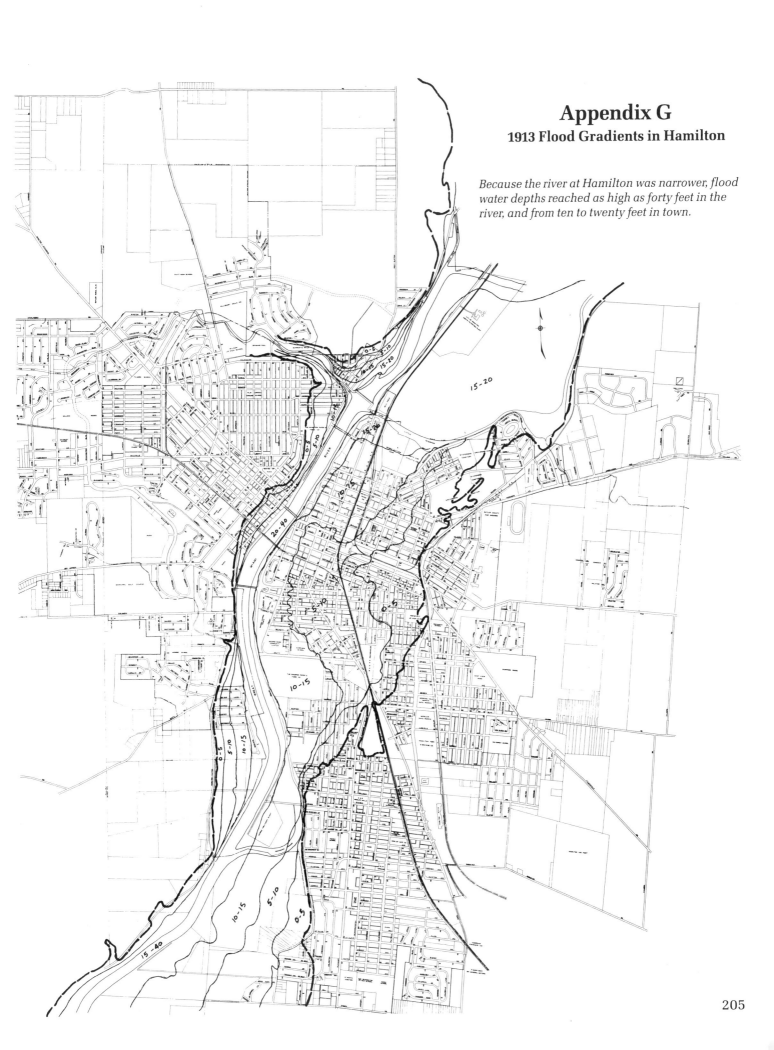

Appendix G
1913 Flood Gradients in Hamilton

Because the river at Hamilton was narrower, flood water depths reached as high as forty feet in the river, and from ten to twenty feet in town.

Appendix H

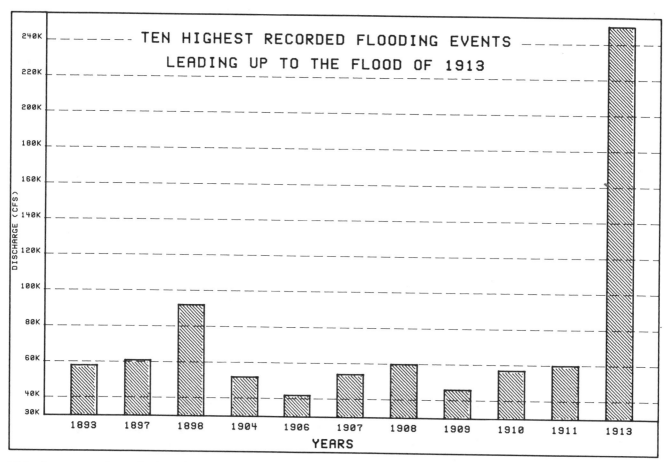

This chart shows the ten highest floods of the Great Miami River between the start of record keeping in 1893 and the great flood of 1913. Historical data also indicates flooding during the years 1805, 1814, 1828, 1832, 1847, 1866, 1882, 1883 and 1884 but accurate measurements were not kept. The chart shows flooding as a measure of flow. For example, normal low flow fluctuates between 500 and 1000 cubic feet per second (cfs). Depending on the area in question, the river tends to leave its natural channel and spill over its banks at approximately 2000 to 3000 cfs.

A major flood of the Great Miami River would have occurred in 1959 had it not been for the Miami Conservancy District's flood protection. Engineers estimate that downtown Hamilton and Dayton would have been covered with five to twenty feet of water (shaded areas) that year had it not been for the District's works. In Hamilton, the Miami University campus, the sewage treatment plant, Mercy Hospital and the electric plant, for example, all would have been flooded. In Dayton, flood waters would have inundated Sinclair Community College, St. Elizabeth Hospital, the Montgomery County courts complex and Fire Department headquarters, among others. The charts at right show estimated depths and areas that would have been flooded in Hamilton (on left) and Dayton.

Appendix I
1959 Highwater in Dayton and Hamilton
Without Flood Protection

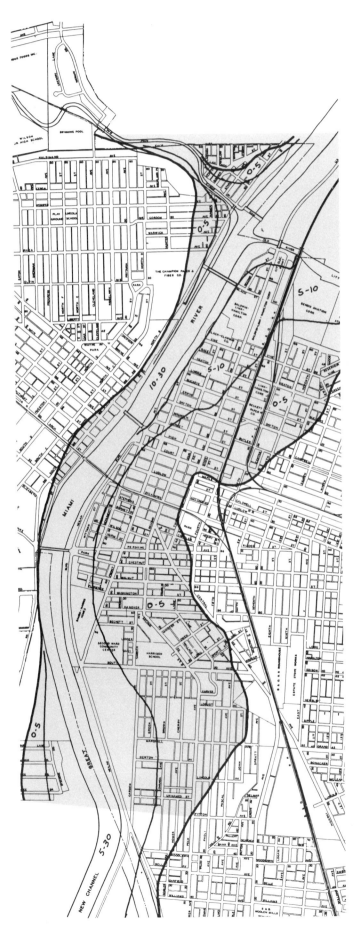

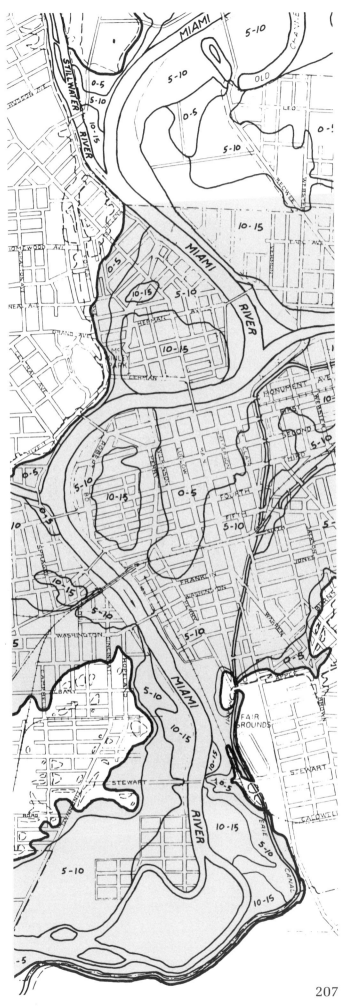

About The Authors

Carl M. Becker, Ph. D., is Professor of History at Wright State University. A native of Miamisburg, Ohio, he is, he asserts, a Buckeye in his bone and marrow. A specialist in Ohio history, he is the author of the book, *The Village: A History of Germantown, Ohio, 1804-1976,* which in 1981 received an award from the Ohio Association of Historical Societies and Museums as the "Best History of a Local Community" for that year. He is the co-editor of a forthcoming book being published by the Ohio University Press, *Hearth and Knapsack: The Ladley Letters, 1857-1880.* He has had numerous articles published in scholarly journals on life in the Miami Valley during the nineteenth century.

Patrick B. Nolan is a native Minnesotan who has moved from the North Woods to the Buckeye state. He received his undergraduate education at Minnesota's Carleton College in Northfield and his Ph. D. from the University of Minnesota in 1971. He joined the History Department of the University of Wisconsin-River Falls, where he taught and administered a regional research archive. In 1973 he moved to Dayton to serve as head of Archives and Special Collections and adjunct associate professor of History at Wright State University. He has published books on the Wright Brothers and on vigilantes and horsethieves in the West. He is an active member of historical and archival associations in several states.